oblivious to a
before.

'Oh please, dear Go
do anything for you, an
him. I will devote the rest of
any way I can, only please God,
him, don't let him die.' And so I prayed, on and
on, not daring to stop. I felt the whole of myself
was transported in those minutes, and that I had
indeed made a pact with God.

## About the Author

Elizabeth Despard Ward, MBE, was brought up in the Sussex countryside amongst ponies, dogs and rabbits and consequently has remained a countrywoman all her life. Married with two daughters and four grandchildren, she was educated at Cheltenham Ladies College, and after many years as an ordinary housewife she became involved in things commercial, doing a variety of jobs, both paid and unpaid, which include being a volunteer for prison after-care magistrate, public relations officer, sales director, SSAFA representative, chicken farmer and car salesman. A keen tennis player and opera buff, Elizabeth Ward lives in Hampshire. She became a Member of the Order of the British Empire in 1978.

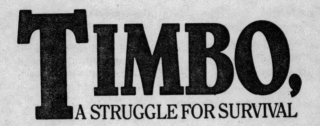

# TIMBO,
## A STRUGGLE FOR SURVIVAL

# Elizabeth Ward

**NEW ENGLISH LIBRARY**
Hodder and Stoughton

**For Nigel
in appreciation of his
great patience,
generosity,
and love**

Copyright © 1986 by Elizabeth
D. Ward

First published in Great Britain
in 1986 by Sidgwick and
Jackson Limited

First paperback edition
published in 1988 by New
English Library for Sidgwick and
Jackson Limited
*Fourth impression 1990*

**British Library C.I.P.**

Ward, Elizabeth D. (Elizabeth
Despard)
  Timbo: a struggle for survival.
  1. Kidney patients. Care –
  Personal observations
  I. Title
  362.1'.97461'00924

ISBN 0-450-42595-9

Printed and bound in Great Britain
for Hodder and Stoughton
Paperbacks, a division of Hodder
and Stoughton Ltd., Mill Road,
Dunton Green, Sevenoaks, Kent
TN13 2YA (Editorial Office: 47
Bedford Square, London, WC1B
3DP) by Richard Clay Ltd.,
Bungay, Suffolk.

# Contents

Say not, the struggle nought availeth,
   The labour and the wounds are vain,
The enemy faints not, nor faileth,
   And as things have been, things remain.

If hopes were dupes, fears may be liars;
   It may be, in yon smoke concealed,
Your comrades chase e'en now the fliers,
   And, but for you, possess the field.

For while the tired waves, vainly breaking,
   Seem here no painful inch to gain,
Far back through creeks and inlets making
   Came, silent, flooding in, the main,

And not by eastern windows only,
   When daylight comes, comes in the light,
In front the sun climbs slow, how slowly,
   But westward, look, the land is bright.

*Arthur Hugh Clough (1819–1861)*

# Acknowledgements

No man is an island and very little of importance can be accomplished alone. Despite Timbo's courage and will to live he might never have survived without the support and encouragement of his doctors, family and friends. In the same way, the British Kidney Patient Association could never have come into being without the support and encouragement of my many friends in renal medicine, and I would like to take this opportunity of thanking them. I would like to pay especial tribute to Timbo's first doctor at Guy's Hospital, John Trounce, who cared for us both with love and diligence over several years; Stewart Cameron, Professor of renal medicine at Guy's Hospital, who took over the task of Timbo's care and for many years has been my champion and confidant in matters concerning the BKPA; Mick Bewick, the charismatic transplant surgeon responsible for Timbo's first and second transplants, whose amazing optimism carried us through many dark days; David Kerr, the Dean of the Hammersmith Hospital, London, who as Chairman of my Grants Committee has given so much time and thought to the work involved (and has taken the trouble to ensure I steer a reasonably straight course!); Richard White, Paediatric Nephrologist at the Children's Hospital, Birmingham; Cyril Chantler, Professor of Paediatric Nephrology at Guy's Hospital, London; Douglas Briggs, Nephrologist at the Western Infirmary, Glasgow and Tony Wing, Nephrologist at St Thomas's Hospital, London for always being there when I needed them. I am indebted beyond words to Laurence Scragg, my colleague and friend, who has helped me over the past eight years to ensure the success of the Association and whose loyalty and companionship have been invaluable. My thanks and admiration go to Carol Marshall who has typed and re-typed the manuscript from double spacing to single spacing and back again with cheerful enthusiasm, and has so identified herself with her work that it has become 'our' book. No list of acknowledgements would be complete without mention of my younger daughter Becky, who showed her love and concern in a practical way over a long period; I shall always be in her debt for the moral support she gave me time and time again.

# Preface

To be asked to write the Preface to an autobiography is an unusual honour; whatever the story may be it is essentially personal, even private. So it requires a great deal of trust on the part of the author and, in my view at least, a respect for integrity on both sides. And this book, as those who read it will quickly recognize, is infinitely more than an autobiography. I am sure that the story Elizabeth Ward has written will reach out beyond itself, as she so clearly desires that it shall, and will become yet one more pledge of ultimate victory in the struggle she so vividly portrays. For it is a continuing struggle described here. It is a struggle which still needs far more massive support than it has yet received from those who have responsibility in government, in the medical profession, and in the whole community of citizens. I shall not spoil the story by anticipating its impact on those who read it. But I must try at least to justify the honour done me by the author.

Some twelve years ago, when I was Bishop of Stepney in East London, I found myself increasingly disturbed by what seemed to me the failure of the Christian Church (not just the Church of England) to give effective leadership on the complex *moral* issues created by scientific and technological discovery. I wrote an article in *The Times* which I entitled 'An Ethical Think-tank'. I suggested that, because of the complexity of moral and ethical issues thrown up by *all* scientific and technological advance, it was impossible (and undesirable) for the Church to imagine that it alone had the authority or the expertise, or even the minimal wisdom, required to give some guidance to those involved in handling the new challenges confronting humanity. I was pleading, in fact, for a 'think-tank' of representative philosophers, scientists, doctors, theologians, and lawyers, etc, to come together to share their own views and vision; to pool their experiences and so speak with an authority which would be a *self-authenticating* authority. Naturally it was in the field of medical science that many of these new ethical problems were emerging with bewildering speed – and still are.

I think that it was as a result of this article that I was asked to participate in meetings of a specially selected commission dealing with the subject of renal transplantation and its implications in the field of morality, law, and religion. And it was thus that I became actively involved in the foundation of The British Kidney Patient Association, and one of its two 'sponsors'.

There is no need for me to spell out what the BKPA is and does; that is the subject of this book. For, in the truest sense, Elizabeth Ward *is* the BKPA. Without her it would not exist; she is its 'onlie begetter'. Yet the really exciting thing about it is that it is not dependent on her; it has its own vigorous and expanding and adventurous life. But it has it *because* of her complete and absolute commitment to the cause; her endlessly creative vision of 'new fields to conquer' and her boundless enthusiasm.

She is, in fact, a person who embodies one of the Christian virtues which is in very short supply today – the virtue of hope. Let me explain what I mean. There is all the difference in the world between 'hoping for the best', or thinking 'whilst there's life there's hope', or 'hoping *against* hope', and the real thing: for hope is a virtue quite literally *rooted in God*. It is a *theological* virtue. It therefore creates its own certainty about a cause or a struggle or an adventure, for that certainty is God-centred.

Again, the reality that I am expressing in an abstract way is the theme and substance of this book. And the book could only have been written in the way it has because the writer is one who believes absolutely in God and his purposes.

Yet, to hope in God is immensely costly. In the case of Elizabeth and her son Timbo, the cost has been, and will continue to be paid in the courage of human suffering, human courage (of an extraordinary quality), and human triumph. I pray that those who read this remarkable story will themselves be led to thank God (as I do) for what Timbo and his mother have achieved for human dignity in our day. It is an immense achievement. I dare not say any more for fear of spoiling, even in the smallest degree, the book as it stands. It has been one of my greatest privileges to know and – in such a limited way – to work with Elizabeth Ward and the Association she founded and continues to inspire.

*The Rt Revd Trevor Huddleston C.R.*           *January 1986*

# Introduction

When my son Timothy first went on haemodialysis, his chances of survival were thought not to be very good. He was seventeen years old, and he had all the strength and courage and will to live usual to a boy of that age, but he also had pericarditis, pleurisy and peritonitis, and dialysis was an essential, desperate measure.

The hospital would not allow me to be with him, nor were they very keen for me to ring. He was to have six hours' dialysis for the first time, and the danger was that he could haemorrhage into his heart. I lived thirty-eight miles, or one hour, away from where he lay fighting for his life. I sat by the telephone and, braving the reactions of the Sister, I rang the unit every hour. I was told quite firmly not to ring again; they would ring me in two hours' time.

It was late July and harvest time. I left the house and wandered out into the fields. I had been numb with fear, incapable of coherent thought, but suddenly, surrounded by full summer with all its beauty, I was brought back to my senses. My son, my only son, was dying, and I was doing nothing, nothing to help him. Overwhelmed by my own fears and wretchedness, I had left him to fight his battle alone. I had reached the centre of a huge cornfield, recently harvested, and I stopped and dropped on to my knees in the open, oblivious to all, and prayed as I had never prayed before.

'Oh please, dear God, don't let him die, don't let him die. I will do anything for you, anything at all, only save him. I will devote the rest of my life to helping in any way I can, only please God, spare him, save him, don't let him die.' And so I prayed, on and on, not daring to stop. I felt the whole of myself was transported in those minutes, and that I had indeed made a pact with God.

That was more than fifteen years ago; God has kept his side of the bargain and I am still trying to keep mine.

# 1

# In the Beginning...

Timbo was born Timothy Nigel Pierce on 3 January 1953 in our huge double bed at Harston Hall in Leicestershire. The second child of a family of three, he was our first and only son – much wanted and much loved. A contented, friendly baby with a winning smile turned readily to laughter, he made up for in charm what he lacked in looks. I, of course, thought he was the most beautiful baby boy that had ever graced a photographer's studio, but I may have been biased – although early snapshots show him with his funny little face always wreathed in smiles. I religiously sent the latest studio portrait of him each year to all his godparents and I remember a telephone call from his godmother, Pam Heber-Percy, who rang to thank me the year he was two.

'I am so pleased, darling, that he is so improved, you must be delighted. Let's face it, he was no oil-painting when he was tiny, was he?'

I was not hurt, I was just very surprised that two people could view the same object so differently!

By the time we left Leicestershire his younger sister Becky had been born, and with thirteen months between them, at nearly four and just five, we sent them to a small dame-school near our new home in Hampshire. Timbo kept us all thoroughly entertained with vivid details of his exploits at school, the battles he had won single-handed in the playground against an army of boys, usually twice his age and size! At that stage they both came home for lunch and his fascinating accounts of his morning adventures were constantly interrupted by a high-pitched indignant treble from his younger sister. 'No Timbo, you didn't. That's not true,' or, 'I didn't see Mrs Adams slam your fingers in the desk.' The thread of the story was usually lost as he turned his attention to his errant sister who had dared to challenge his word. I thought it all highly amusing but his father took quite a different view.

'If you continue to encourage him to tell such lies, it won't be long before he cannot himself recognize the truth,' he would warn me.

'Oh but darling, he's only weaving fairy stories,' I would plead. 'Don't be hard on him, he's only five and he is sure to grow out of it.'

By the time he was six he was staying all day. Becky was still returning home for lunch and I noticed that suddenly all the excitements took place in the afternoons! He came home one day with a black eye, which I heard later from the headmistress had been the result of a tumble in the school playground. The story I heard from him was much more thrilling.

'We were roaring down Worldham Hill in the school bus and I was sitting behind the driver when suddenly a huge black dog sprang out in front of us. The driver slammed on his brakes and I fell forward banging my head on the back of his seat. I was very brave and didn't cry at all.'

I used to meet the bus at the bottom of our long drive every afternoon at 4 o'clock and we would walk back up together hand in hand, whilst I listened spellbound to the amazing events of his day. I was a little late one afternoon and turning the corner at the top of our drive I was in time to see the bus disappearing down the road. Timbo saw me from the bottom of the drive, removed his cap with a heavy action and, wiping his small hand across his brow, said as he approached, 'Phew, that was some walk. I missed the bus and walked all the way from Alton.' Since Alton was over four miles away and I had just seen the bus disappearing out of sight, I thought the time had come to have a little friendly talk.

By the time he was seven, with only a year to go before he went away to boarding school, he was already making it clear that the academic side of life was not for him. We decided that a year at a pre-prep school, where the emphasis was on learning and not on play, might help to uncover his latent scholastic skills. At the end of his first term at the new school we went together to the parents' evening. Whilst I gazed dreamily at his single contribution on the festooned walls, Nigel flicked sternly through his exercise books.

'Tell me, Miss Pritchard, how is Timothy shaping this term from a work point of view?' he asked.

A look of positive adoration came into her eyes as she replied, 'Oh Mr Ward, he's such a dear little boy. So helpful and sweet. Do you know he's the only boy who always offers to carry...'

My husband interrupted. 'Yes, I am sure he's very helpful but, Miss Pritchard, his work, his work, how is his work getting on?'

She seemed unruffled by the interruption and continued, 'Oh, his work's all right, but he is so helpful, he always cleans the blackboard for me and offers to tidy my desk. Such a dear, kind, helpful little boy,' she repeated.

His father was unimpressed. 'Any excuse I suppose to save him from getting his head down to some proper work,' was his retort.

'But darling, he's only seven. Don't be so hard on him,' I urged him to relent.

'In another ten years you will be saying he's only seventeen and what then?' was his reply.

His four and a half years at Sunningdale Prep School were some of the happiest years of my life. He made all the school teams from the Under Tens in his first term, to becoming captain of all but one in his last. Nearly every Wednesday and Saturday afternoon throughout the winter terms Nigel and I would drive over to where the match was being held and shout ourselves hoarse on the touch-line. On hot summer

days we would sit in deck-chairs or lie on the grass, listening
to the click of the willow and idly chatting to the boys sitting
around us awaiting their turn to bat. Work was an effort,
which he did not often make, but he found his *métier* on the
playing-fields and was immensely happy and well-liked,
though he no doubt drove his masters wild with despair at his
carefree attitude to the class-room.

In the summer of 1966, with his Common Entrance behind
him, he was looking forward to a new school with new friends
to make and challenges ahead. A simple entry in my diary on
16 September 1966 reads: 'Harrow term begins. Dr McGill
for Timbo.' Thus began a long, hard battle for us all.

All three children were moving on in their educational
careers: Susie from Cheltenham Ladies College to Bristol
University to read law; Becky from the local dame-school to
Wycombe Abbey; and Timbo from Sunningdale to Harrow.
My husband's work involved business with Holland and that
summer holiday found all five of us on a scent barge on the
Dutch canals. We awoke one morning outside Utrecht to find
that Timbo was complaining of a sore throat. His eyelids
were strangely puffy and he could scarcely speak, but after
the initial pangs of natural worry I decided for the sake of the
others to resist the temptation of calling in the nearest doctor.
Well before the end of our holiday the sore throat had
disappeared. On our return from Holland, Timbo continued
his normal holiday activities: shooting, bicycling, volley-ball,
and swimming with friends and sisters.

As the start of the new term drew near he greeted it with a
mixture of excitement and apprehension. His room at
Harrow already contained his own desk, bookcase, and
chair, his trunk was packed, and the evening before his
departure for the great adventure of public school I asked
him to weigh himself. I was in his bedroom putting the final
touches to his packing when he called. He was standing on the
scales, remarking in wonderment that his weight had increased
by nearly a stone during the eight-week summer holiday. I
could only stand and stare at his legs, which I noticed for the

first time looked full, the skin was shiny and tight, and all natural shape had disappeared. Fear manifests itself in a number of strange ways: the near-miss of an oncoming car produces tingles in the wrists, the ringing of the telephone bell too late at night still causes my heart to miss a beat and brings me closer to the understanding of the words 'cold fear'; the news of my children's sudden ills has always made my heart race and the blood thunder in my ears, but as I stood in the bathroom that Thursday nineteen years ago all these feelings overwhelmed me as my instinct told me something was frighteningly wrong.

I rang our local GP only to find that he was away on holiday and an unknown locum in his place. I called first one, then another doctor friend of ours, neither of whom were in, and all the time I could feel my panic mounting. In desperation I rang the locum and explained. I was told to bring a sample of Timbo's urine to the surgery in the morning for testing, but that Timbo himself must remain in bed. Even through my fear I was able to protest that this was impossible as he was leaving for his new school later that day! My horror at the possibility that Timbo might not get to school with the others on the first day of term was balanced by fear and anguish caused by his condition. A fun-loving, football-kicking fellow who had never taken work seriously and lived only for the playing-fields, he had been tutored for three full holidays in order to pass the Common Entrance exam, but now it seemed as if all his efforts were to be in vain. Like most mothers, I understood only pain, fever or sickness, and it was many months before I could accept that a boy who seemed himself and complained of nothing could be so desperately ill.

That first sleepless night was one of many as the years slipped by. The simple test at the surgery confirmed my worst fears that something was indeed wrong and there was to be no school for Timbo that day. A specialist was called and the verdict was pronounced: 'You can forget this first term. The boy has acute nephritis [an inflammation of the kidneys] which could clear up within two and six weeks, and until the kidneys stop leaking protein, the temperature drops to normal, and the swelling in his ankles disappears, he must have complete bed rest.' I remember that Timbo's own reaction to this devastating pronouncement was relief that he had not been carted off to hospital.

That afternoon Morecambe and Wise were filming at a disused railway station some two miles from our home. Becky persuaded me to cycle over with her and see the fun, which I did with great reluctance. It was to be the first of many occasions when I accompanied her in person but my heart and mind were somewhere else. Poor little girl, how she must have suffered during those early years. How could I give her the attention she deserved, concerned myself with her anxieties and despair, shared as I should have done in her triumphs and disasters, when all the time my only son could not make up his mind whether to die on that Monday or the next? The girls departed for the term and we were left to pick up the pieces of a shattered dream.

So began a life filled with more tutors, intake and output charts, endless doctors' visits, and a constant search to find a way to fill each dreary waking hour. Timbo himself settled into his new life with amazing ease. The daily tutor sat by his bed each morning filling the reluctant mind with History, French, and English until relief came with a break for lunch and an hour or two of games – chess, Monopoly, Cluedo, Vingt-et-un – the list was endless, all were tried in turn. When Becky went away to boarding school leaving behind her a sick and much-beloved brother, I tried to think of ways to bridge the gap between us. 'Look at the moon,' I said. 'When it is bright you will know that I am looking at it too. We can say our good-nights to each other through the moon and keep in touch that way.' There were many times in those two and a half months when Timbo lay dying at home that I longed for the bright moonlit nights so that I could enjoy the peace of sharing thoughts with her.

By mid-November the words of the visiting consultant

rang daily through my head. 'Between two and six weeks' had been his prophecy for when all would be well and Timbo once more back on his feet, a normal, healthy boy again. In the seventh week I begged our family doctor to call in the specialist once more since it was obvious, even to me, that things were wrong. His intake of fluid continued to exceed his output, showing that his kidneys were not able to cope with the amount of fluid he was drinking. The doctor assured me that 'these things take time' and refused to contact the specialist. I am sure Timbo's life was saved when our local doctor went off on holiday once more and the locum reappeared. He arrived one Friday morning for the regular weekly visit and asked me when Timbo had last had his blood taken. I was surprised by the question and assured him that, apart from the occasion some months back when his illness was first diagnosed, a sample of his blood had never been asked for. The locum took blood and drove himself with it to the local hospital and rang me that night to say that he had asked the specialist to visit the following morning as the situation had now become serious. For me, the situation had not altered since early September and I found it hard to grasp the meaning of his words.

I remember my crazy, impassioned plea to the consultant and the GP, who were trying desperately to control me in the hallway downstairs: 'Please, please don't take him to hospital.' I was sure he would never return to me from there. The shock of realizing that not only was Timbo's health failing to improve but it was actually deteriorating filled me with such despair that my immediate reaction was to deny the situation.

We were granted a reprieve of twenty-four hours in order that his little sister could see him on her school leave-out, and by that Sunday night Timbo had begun the first of his innumerable hospital admissions and I a long, if broken, vigil at the side of his hospital bed.

The consultant explained with kindness that Timbo was extremely sick. The acute kidney condition that was originally diagnosed was in fact a kidney disease of far greater seriousness, and in reply to my inevitable question it was revealed to me that since our local doctor had never again contacted the specialist he had naturally assumed that all was well. They kept him at Winchester Hospital for three days undergoing tests, until they realized that a renal biopsy was essential.

I remember so well the afternoon we drove him to Guy's Hospital in London. He wore his new school overcoat which was now several sizes too large, for the first time, over his pyjamas, and as usual he was uncomplaining and resigned. He felt exceedingly ill and walking was a difficulty, so it is not hard to imagine my distress when I reached Guy's to find that there were long, seemingly endless, corridors to be negotiated underground from one part of the hospital to another. I found myself on our arrival at the hospital only concerned with the need to get Timbo off his feet and into bed, and to arrange his private television for him. The seriousness of his situation took second place.

We were all covered by private health insurance and I had naturally assumed that Timbo would go into a private ward where I could sit with him and continue my care of him. I was, of course, most distressed to learn that there was no renal medicine being carried out privately and, therefore, no alternative but for him to go into a general ward. Fortunately, at the age of thirteen he was too old for the children's ward and too young to be with the men, so he was given a side-ward to himself and we were seldom apart.

Much has been said by others about the caring, love, and compassion shown by doctors and nursing staff to patients and relatives in hospital. I think that such bouquets are often handed out when barely earned, since fear and relief can loosen our tongues in curious ways. However, I can say with truth after the passage of so much time that the kindness, compassion, and understanding that was shown to us by consultants, doctors, and nurses at Guy's Hospital did much to smooth the path and ease the pain over the years of our visits there.

The results of the biopsy showed severe scarring to both his kidneys, and the disease that had swept unchecked across the living tissue threatened to continue its path of destruction. I can see the doctor now, sitting on the end of an iron bedstead in a small, empty ward, one foot planted firmly on the ground, the other swinging backwards and forwards, backwards and forwards like a pendulum ticking away the hours of life. I sat with Nigel beside me, staring at the floor and fighting back the tears, trying hard to make some meaning of the words that flowed from the doctor's mouth. Expressions like 'the only course open to us' froze my mind and forced me back to prayer. That Timbo should stay with us was all that mattered and 'death' was the only word we understood. It was decided that a powerful drug called Cyclophosphamide with dangerous side-effects, untried on one so young, should be used in a desperate bid to arrest the course of the disease. The words 'dialysis', the means of cleansing the blood artificially by the use of a machine, and 'transplantation' were as yet strangers to my vocabulary.

I think for Timbo one of the greatest hardships that he had to face at that time was the separation from his golden retriever, Zooloo. He had called her after the famous film of that name, although with a different spelling, and had written to me from prep school three years before, letting me know of his decision. The Christmas holidays loomed ahead and we had been told that our only hope of having Timbo with us over Christmas time was to move to London. His condition was too serious for the doctors to consider our taking him back to our home in Hampshire, so between hospital visits, preparations for Christmas, and the girls' home-coming I began searching for a London house to rent. It was inconceivable that we should leave his dog behind and as my search progressed I continually came face to face with that

well-known sign 'no dogs or children'. At last my persever-
ance was rewarded and I found a house in Egerton Crescent,
large enough to accommodate us all and with an American
owner sympathetic to Timbo's need for Zooloo.

Light appeared at last in the heavy-clouded sky and with
the London house secured, friendly smiles of hope on the
faces of the doctors, and Timbo on his feet and out of bed for
the first time in three and a half months helping with
Christmas preparations on the ward, I looked forward with
eagerness and joy to welcoming all my children back for
Christmas. The joy was short-lived. The obvious side-effect
of the drug had begun to rear its ugly head. Timbo was losing
his hair in clumps, and whilst there was not a word of
complaint from him I knew, of course, the measure of his
misery. Constant blood tests showed that his white blood
count was dangerously low and, hospitals being a well-
known and accepted source of infection, it was agreed that he
should be discharged as soon as possible.

I had returned home that afternoon before his release from
hospital to finish the packing for the move to London. Susie
was back from Bristol University and was on her knees with
me in the drawing-room wrapping presents for the family and
friends. Because of my involvement with Timbo and my
almost constant presence at the hospital the dogs had not
been walked for several weeks. Cook popped her head round
the drawing-room door and asked if she should take the dogs
for a short walk. I replied, 'No, don't worry. Susie and I will
take them.'

We walked together down the drive, across the road, and
on to the large open common. Moving this way and that,
sterns waving, the dogs were soon out of sight. Later, with the
little dog beside us, we stood waiting for Zooloo's return
when suddenly I saw her. First a flash of yellow and then a
lighter shade of the bracken through which she ran – tail
streaming, ears flat back against her head, she arrived with
the speed of a jaguar and dropped dead at my feet. I looked
down at her aghast. Her body twitched twice and then lay still

with the same half-smile on her face that had shown on the run towards us. Was it a heart attack? We were never to know. Susie fell on her knees beside this beautiful dog in an agony of despair. I lifted her and with my arm tightly around her shaking shoulders, we walked back together to the house. It was all there waiting to come out: the anger, the horror, the pain. My poor beloved Timbo had suffered so much and now this; how was I to tell him? Susie had gone to her room to weep alone and my pent-up feelings were allowed full rein. I ran to Nigel howling with a mixture of rage and misery and I beat my bare fists on his chest: 'Oh God, how could you do this to him? What has he done to deserve it? What have I done to deserve it? Tell me, oh, tell me, God, let me understand.' Zooloo was collected and buried in the garden and we drove with heavy hearts to Guy's Hospital.

Daily for the past two weeks Timbo had shared with us his excitement at the thought of getting back to Zooloo. He never spoke of the illness, nor did he mention the girls. Even Christmas seemed of little consequence, but his precious dog was the focal point of all his longings. I knew how much he would want to say his goodbyes with dignity so I couldn't break such shattering news just as he was leaving the hospital. I also knew that it would be too cruel to allow him to think that she would be there to greet him on his arrival at the London house, so it was decided that I should go straight to the hospital that evening and tell him of Zooloo's death, although knowing that he would have to lie with his misery alone through the long, dark night. It was bath time when I arrived and I went with him to the bathroom. I knelt on the floor running my hands through the warm water, gathering the courage to break the news as best I could.

'I have some bad news for you darling, I'm afraid.'

He looked up at me out of huge black-rimmed eyes and asked, 'Is it Zooloo?'

'Yes,' I said.

'She's dead, isn't she? Oh well, everything seems to be going wrong for me just now.'

I looked down at this son of mine, whose future had been so assured, and I saw a small, tired skeleton of a child, thin bony hands clenched in the water, bald head bowed, fighting bravely to hold back the tears, and I thought, 'Oh God, if he can live through this I doubt I can.'

Those Christmas holidays were a nightmare but we did our best to carry on as near normal as was humanly possible. Timbo had his first blood transfusion and I can see him now sitting up in bed in his striped pyjamas, left forearm firmly strapped in position whilst the right hand busied itself writing his term's exams for his tutor. Talks with his caring and understanding consultant, John Trounce, had convinced us that the right thing to do was to hang a 'business as usual' notice round his neck, which we did, and when he was old enough and able to take over the management of his own life, he firmly left it there. The loss of his hair was devastating for us all and his only comment was to draw on scraps of paper small, round, sad faces with bald heads and tears splashing onto flat cheeks. Timbo was allowed only infrequent nights with us and for the rest of those holidays he was in and out of hospital whilst the doctors did their best to stabilize his worsening condition.

A countrywoman all my life, I found the confines of the city an added burden and paced the small, enclosed, private garden with my cocker spaniel each morning, like a caged lion. Eventually the girls departed for school and, joy of joys, we returned to the country and our anxious friends. The local doctor, whose stubborn ignorance had nearly cost my son his life, had in our absence been taken by death himself, so robbing me of my vengeance.

Now that we had left Guy's, except for fortnightly clinics, I had a chance to look around me and survey the wreckage of my life. Up to the onset of Timbo's illness I had been Sales Director of our own family firm, and as a hobby enjoyed the company of a small gathering of Jersey nurse-cows playing mother not only to their own calves, but to young Friesians bought in the local market. My involvement with Timbo had been absolute and I realized that, faced with five empty Jersey cows, the time had come to find another hobby. So, reluctantly, I sold them. Nigel had already accepted the necessity of looking for a new Sales Director, so in a matter of six short months my whole life had changed and my world became centred on Timbo's illness.

With much trepidation and unwillingness, I finally agreed to take Timbo alone with me to the Canary Islands on what our doctor termed 'a convalescent trip'. In the many years of an ideally happy marriage it was the first occasion that I had been separated from Nigel, except through work, and the prospect filled me with apprehension. In the first place, I had no desire to leave my husband, who had been such a pillar of support through all the months of wretchedness, and nor did I relish the prospect of shouldering alone the responsibility for Timbo's condition. During the long, dark months we had discussed the possibility of going when he was better – to places where the sun shone and we could all relax and grow young again. Bathing and boating trips, picnics on golden sands, the gentle lap of a lazy sun-soaked sea, these would be ours when the right time came, but always it would be the three of us.

However, our holiday together was in a way successful. I weathered the separation from my husband and seeing Timbo full of smiles and laughter, enjoying the activities that his frailty allowed, I took courage and began to accept the miracle of waking each morning at the start of a new day to find that Timbo was still there to share it with me.

# 2

# Dialysis or Death

At the beginning of the summer term in 1967 Timbo joined the other new boys at Harrow. He was not only nearly a year older than the other new arrivals, but he was also nearly bald. Roll call was taken daily and boaters were lifted as the boys filed past a senior prefect affirming their names and I always thought what strength of arm it must have taken in those early days for him to lift his boater. He was, of course, boys being what they are, the object of much cruel teasing and derision. 'Baldy' was their favourite name for him, but nothing could destroy his obvious delight on returning to a normal life. Unfortunately, his place at Harrow had been earned by his ability on the playing-fields not in the classroom and great was the sarcasm of his Housemaster when he learned that, much to Timbo's own bitter disappointment, he was not allowed to participate in any sporting activities that first term. He was still on a high protein diet, too, and ham and cheese rolls had to be fitted in between the morning lessons and the normal meals. It was with no feeling of compensation that he wended his way to the tea-rooms each afternoon for cream buns and milk shakes, whilst the other boys ran in track suits and cricket gear to the squash-courts and playing fields.

He was quite unable to keep the tremor from his voice when he rang me half-way through his first term and told me that his Housemaster had said, 'You have no right to be in a decent school for proper boys, you should be in a home for cripples. If you had only one arm or one leg we could understand; you look like other boys but you are not.' It was all Nigel could do to restrain me from driving to the school and demanding to see the Headmaster then and there. I refrained because I believed Nigel when he told me that Timbo would only be made to suffer more. I notched up another form of torture experienced, but kept both my counsel and my sanity.

One of the bugbears during those four chequered years at Harrow was the accumulation of fluid in his feet and legs. He so longed to be 'a proper boy' that he spared himself nothing in terms of his health, joining in all that he was allowed and dreading the times when Matron would ring me and advise his temporary removal from school because of his inability to cope with daily life. When he knew the fluid was getting the better of him, anxious to avoid the invalid weeks which he knew awaited him for as long as possible, he would set his alarm for the early hours and lie on his bed with his legs up on the wall draining the fluid from his feet so that he could get his shoes on and tie them up before reporting for breakfast with the others.

He had joined the Corps at Harrow and was, I think, a reasonably enthusiastic member. One of the highlights, and no doubt rewards, was the annual Corps camp which in the summer of 1968 was to be held in Germany. He was, like the others, much looking forward to the week's camp and was bitterly disappointed and distressed when Sir Alan Outram, the young master detailed to accompany the boys, declared his unwillingness to accept the responsibility of taking Timbo with them. His life at that time at Harrow threatened to become all work and no play and I was determined that this was one experience he was not going to miss. I telephoned John Trounce, the wonderfully sympathetic, understanding doctor at Guy's Hospital who had been looking after him for the past two years, and begged him to set Sir Alan's mind at rest. This he successfully achieved, and Timbo joined the other boys at Corps camp for one of the best weeks in his life.

I naturally spent most of the week concerning myself with the effects of damp and strenuous exercise on damaged kidneys, but he turned up on time at the appointed meeting-place wearing dark glasses and an air of satisfaction, and in reply to my question, 'Did you learn any German whilst you were over there?' said, 'Yes, *vollen Sie tanzen!*'

During this time of concern for his future and the day to day anxiety caused by his deteriorating condition as the disease continued its relentless destruction of his kidneys, there was another blade added to the knife that was already cutting me in two: the problem of our relationship with one another. His dependence on me and his need for me when, as a young boy, he had first become ill had only served to strengthen our bond of love and to deepen our feelings for each other. Now the call of distant manhood and the attitude of those around him at school made him question his closeness to me. Because of our regular trips to clinic, the necessity of supervising his drugs, and my own anxious attitude, it was impossible for me to slip, as all mothers should at that time, into a pleasing backdrop of helpfulness only to be called upon when needed.

As the terms went by he became more and more resentful of the need for regular meetings with his mother. At first his friendly greeting and bright chatter made me look forward with eagerness to our regular visits to the clinic at Guy's. We would meet at Pont Street Mews at the house of an old friend, he having arrived by underground from Harrow-on-the-Hill and I by car. The journey on was full of talk and laughter until we arrived at the clinic doors to await our turn in the queue. Often he was in a teasing mood and with delight would extract urgent whispers of remonstration from me as he scribbled on the consultant's notepad in his absence from the room. His attitude then towards his illness was light-hearted, almost casual; he sought distraction from the seriousness of his situation, and found it with ease.

But by the time he was fifteen years old he wanted so much to live a free boy's life, untrammelled by hospital visits, uncluttered by medication and the need for care. I became the embodiment of all his frustrations and limitations and as a result became also his whipping-boy. My eager anticipation of our stolen mid-week hours together turned into dread as each rendezvous approached. No smile of happy recognition as he crossed the Mews yard, no hugs or laughter shared, instead a dark and sullen silence often maintained throughout our journey there and back. The transition from a gay, warm, loving, friendly boy to the quietly cruel, resentful youth was too sudden for me and I was left hurt and shattered.

The time came when his doctors shared with me their fears that no more could be done to preserve the *status quo*. I should feel free, they said, to seek other opinions, they had done their best and the future could not be foretold. There was still no word of 'dialysis' or 'transplantation' and so to us the alternative to a life with renal function was only death. I assured the doctors that there was no opinion that we valued more than theirs but sought their approval to introduce Timbo to Harry Edwards, the famous faith-healer. Much to my relief the idea was greeted with friendly interest and so, with the subject of my daily prayers safely at school, I set about making the arrangements for the laying on of hands.

Two years previously, with much initial scepticism, Timbo had agreed to join the confirmation class with a view to exposing himself to the possibility of God. 'If Spike [his Housemaster] and the Chaplain can convince me that there is a God, I will get confirmed, if not, I won't,' he said. Two lessons before the great occasion, when excited preparations had been made at his House to welcome his illustrious godfather, Earl Mountbatten, Timbo decided that neither the Chaplain nor his Housemaster had been able to convince him of His presence; so, much to everyone's disappointment, he withdrew himself from the confirmation classes at the eleventh hour. It was, therefore, with reservation that I telephoned the Sanctuary in Shere and spoke to Harry Edwards.

'Supposing the patient is not a believer, what then?' I asked.

'I have cured small children and even babies and can tell you positively that it is not necessary for the patient to have faith,' was his reply.

An appointment was made and with a certain amount of trepidation I put my plans to Timbo on his return from school that summer holiday. Amazingly enough he was immensely cooperative, perhaps through curiosity, and consented to allow the faith-healer to 'have a go at getting rid of my fluid', as he put it.

It was with a mixture of feelings that I arrived at Shere with Timbo that hot, summer's day, unsure what to expect both in terms of the company we would be keeping and the miracle that might be performed. Whilst I had no illusions concerning the implications of his kidney disease, my earnest wish was that the laying on of hands would somehow release the fluid and leave him free again.

I had pictured a scene, with paillasses littered about the ground supporting heads in blood-soaked bandages and bodies shaking with the palsy – a mixture perhaps of the New Testament and the Crimean War. I was in for a surprise! The large and beautiful country house standing in its own grounds at the end of a long drive had a small, modern chapel built beside it. We arrived a little late for the appointed time, as usual, and no one was about. I pushed open the chapel door and together we entered and found seats. The place was full and the atmosphere was heavy with expectation and prayer. The patients themselves, and those that loved them, sat together silently watching the door through which the great man would appear. Above the altar hung the well-known painting of Christ with his head slightly on one side, a crown of thorns topping his shoulder-length hair. (In the late 1960s there was a passion for long hair, not only for girls but for boys as well. We were adamant – a boy should look like a boy, not a girl, and Timbo was despatched regularly to the barber.) I was roused from my prayers by an urgent nudge on my left and Timbo, in a piercing whisper which shattered the silence like a pistol-shot, said, 'If it was all right for Him, why isn't it all right for me?'

Whilst, in a sense, nothing was achieved from our meeting with Harry Edwards that afternoon, it was in a way a milestone in my life. It opened my eyes to the realization that, through faith, miracles could indeed be worked providing the physical symptoms had come about through the workings of a troubled mind. Organic disease was perhaps another matter, and whilst I had always been quite sure that a healthy mind could keep a body healthy, it could have no power over the secret destruction of healthy cells. I learnt, too, that afternoon that Timbo's indomitable spirit, which would stand him in good stead in the years ahead, was a force to be respected and catered for if he was not to become swamped by the anxious attitudes of those surrounding him.

His struggles at Harrow ended with the total failure of his kidneys three weeks after the beginning of the summer term when he was seventeen years old. His 'O' levels had been taken the previous summer in the sick-room, in the presence of an invigilator and, incredibly enough, he had passed all but one of the few he took. He had been, it seemed, granted a reprieve and we were hopeful that he would have an uninterrupted summer term and the chance to share in the fun of swimming and the skills of the cricket-field as well as getting his head down to some serious 'A' level preparations. It was not to be: Matron rang to say that he seemed unwell and asked me to drive over and bring him home. A visit to Guy's Hospital next day was to be the last for both of us for many months to come and every word spoken and each scene enacted have been absorbed and imprinted indelibly on my memory.

Timbo's whole body was so distorted with fluid that it was not possible on that day even to do up his shirt. We managed to find one pair of track-suit trousers with an elasticated waist and, with open sandals on his feet, we turned up at the renal clinic for the last time. His kind and loving doctor, whilst

doing his best to placate my fears, urged me to allow Timbo
to be admitted for a few days' observation. A blood test
showed that his kidney function had plummeted and for the
first time I heard the word 'dialysis'. I was quite unprepared
for such developments and my animal instincts got the better
of me. My frozen mind refused to allow me to give up Timbo
despite the patient pleadings of the doctor. Looking back
now I wonder at the kindness and understanding that was
shown me, and which contrasted so sharply with the
treatment I was to receive later elsewhere. Blow upon blow
followed as the doctor explained that, owing to an outbreak
of the dreaded hepatitis, the renal unit was closed to all
newcomers. Arrangements would be made for Timbo to
receive dialysis at a renal unit nearer to our home and in the
meantime I could take him back with me to the country and
await instructions.

Timbo, who had so suddenly changed from a schoolboy
into a full-time renal patient, ended his brave days at Harrow
with a fitting tribute from his new Housemaster. 'In his long
battle with a cruel disease he has, I hope, been helped by his
friends here; but it is we who are all in debt to him for the
shining example he has set of courage and cheerfulness in
disappointment and adversity that could well have daunted
the bravest soul. I cannot recall that he ever failed to produce
a smile of welcome or spoke one word of self-pity.'

In the summer of 1970 we were hurtled without ceremony
and with no time to adjust into the unwelcoming arms of
doctors with a difference. To be fair, the combination of a
patient who arrives with a label around his neck saying 'Guy's
Hospital' – an established seat of learning, the envy of many
provincial hospitals – and a forceful, opinionated mother,
was not the best combination to ensure popularity. We had
come from a warm and friendly place where compassion and
understanding were the order of the day, where the use of
Christian names did much to allay fear, and where the patient
undoubtedly came first. A child, be he seventeen or seven,

who is adjusting to a chronic illness and new treatments cannot progress and flourish if his mother is frightened and unsure. The mother of a sick child should not only be allowed, but should be encouraged, to spend as much time with her child in hospital as is possible for her. She should be drawn into the doctor's confidence, allowed to sit with her child behind the screens during examinations, have explained to her – time and time again if necessary, since fear freezes the mind and blocks the ears – the need for each new treatment, so that she understands and can join the doctor in his fight to save her child's life. In children's hospitals today throughout the country mothers' needs are catered for, but there are too many older children whose chronic sickness has forced their feeling of dependence, who find themselves in adult hospitals where the needs of the adolescent and his mother are neither understood nor catered for.

The passage of time has mercifully blurred the details of the facts surrounding the medical decision taken at St Mary's Hospital, Portsmouth, to allow Timbo to die untreated, leaving me only with a vague impression. No doubt they argued, as renal physicians often do today, that there were medical reasons why dialysis would not be beneficial, but whatever the reasons they were certainly not discussed with me, his mother. John Trounce had steered us in the direction of Portsmouth specifically for Timbo to receive dialysis and yet he was not being prepared for dialysis and his doctor at Portsmouth had not discussed his future treatment either with me or with him. He had pericarditis and pleurisy and was, I knew, desperately ill, but I realized that if his doctor at Guy's reckoned he needed dialysis treatment when he sent him to Portsmouth, he must have needed that treatment even more urgently ten days later.

I left the hospital and my place by his bedside and rang John Trounce at Guy's from a nearby call-box. I was terrified that I was going to lose Timbo and poured out my fears between sobs, begging John to come down to Portsmouth and persuade the renal physician Dolf Polak to treat him.

John answered my plea for help by catching the next train down to Portsmouth and, in so doing, undoubtedly saved Timbo's life. He told me later that the doctors had no experience of dialysing a patient with pericarditis and had decided that the chances were that Timbo would die as a result of treatment. Since he was without question going to die *without* the treatment it was, I felt, a poor reason for denying it. John returned to London, taking with him my undying gratitude and love and the assurance of Dolf Polak that Timbo would be prepared for dialysis later that day, when a shunt would be inserted into his leg.

I had been brought up as a child to view a doctor like a policeman, as a friend, someone I could turn to and trust, and certainly my experience with the doctors with whom I had come into contact at Guy's Hospital had done nothing to change my views. The doctors at Portsmouth were quite another matter and for the first time in my life I came up against the egotistical, self-satisfied traits that are the cause of much patient unhappiness in the renal world. I had committed the unforgivable crime: in trying to save my son's life I had implied that the doctor looking after him was not omnipotent and did not know as much as another doctor who had been called in to advise. There had been unacceptable interference with a doctor's decision and I could have expected to suffer for it.

The day before Timbo's great adventure, when he would be connected to the machine which would clean his blood and give him the best chance of survival, I waited anxiously all day for the chance to speak to his doctor. At Portsmouth in those days, and I have no doubt it is the same today, all relatives were ejected from the ward during ward rounds and made to wait patiently until the doctors had passed through. At Guy's Hospital the relatives sat by the bed during the ward round and were, therefore, in a position to ask questions of the visiting team which helped to calm fears and give confidence. Apart from the fact that I had been told by John Trounce that Timbo was to receive his first dialysis on

Friday, neither the Sister on his ward nor his doctor had spent one moment of their time with me explaining his treatment and offering comfort and reassurance.

I sat that morning in the waiting-room, like a dutiful mother, hoping to speak with the doctor after his rounds. Sister knew of my anxiety to speak with him and whether she communicated my wish to the doctor or not I do not know, but when the round was over he walked past the open sitting-room door without a word or a glance in my direction and was gone before I had time to react. He returned to the ward that evening and once again I implored Sister to let me speak with him. On this occasion she promised me that I could. I sat in the waiting-room on Sister's instructions for more than an hour, eating my heart out with fear and worry, until the door opened and Sister's surprised voice broke into my thoughts.

'Good heavens, are you still here? I am afraid the doctor had to leave in a hurry on an urgent matter. One of the registrars will be sending for you later.'

I went slowly back to the ward and sat by Timbo's bed and held his hand and prayed and prayed that whatever it was they were going to do to him tomorrow would be successful and keep him on this earth.

The call from the junior registrar finally came and served only to increase my fears and despair. He was young, inexperienced, nervous and cold.

'I don't know if you are aware how concerned we are about Timothy's condition?' A comforting start. 'We estimate his chances to be in the region of 40/60 since the dangers are that he will haemorrhage into his heart.'

He continued talking to me but I was no longer listening. With my heart pounding in my ears I could only wait like a trapped animal for my chance of escape. When it eventually came I almost ran, unthinking, to the stairway in a sub-conscious plan to put the greatest possible distance between me and the sound of the voice and the implication of the words that I heard. I stopped half-way down the stairs and remembered Timbo. He was still alive and with me, waiting for my return to his bedside. I looked out through the window onto the car park and beyond to the graveyard and thought, not for the first time, of the insensitivity of planning a graveyard next door to a hospital.

I was standing alone, unsuccessfully trying to fight back the tears, when I became conscious of a light and purposeful tread coming up the stairs towards me. The footsteps stopped at my side and a kind and caring voice said, 'Oh dear, oh dear, have we got problems here?' I turned towards the white-coated stranger and the warmth of his voice released the flood and I cried as if my heart would break.

'It's my son,' I sobbed. 'They say he is going to die.'

He put a hand on my shaking shoulders and turned me towards the stairs. 'Who could possibly have told you that? I have never heard anything so ridiculous. Die? Of course he is not going to die, we are going to make him better for you.'

I walked with him to his office where he tried to comfort and reassure me. Of course, the situation was a tricky one, he agreed, but he was positive that in the end all would be well. Timbo was young and strong and had already shown them in so short a time his courage and resilience. Dr Harry Lee became a firm friend and a strong ally and, despite the fact that sadly we got out of step with one another in later years, I will never cease to be grateful to him for the trouble he took that evening to pick me up and stand me on my feet again, and give me hope.

I have shared with so many other mothers the horrors of those early days when end-stage renal failure is first diagnosed in the child we love. But I hope and pray that no mother now will ever know the bewilderment and disbelief, the unnecessary anguish and suffering, caused by lack of awareness and understanding of all things relating to dialysis and the need for treatment. When Timbo was first admitted to the renal unit at Portsmouth he weighed fifty-two kilos and most of that weight was fluid. By the process of dialysis, about which I knew nothing at all, his weight was reduced over a period of six weeks so that once more he became a small, sunken-eyed skeleton, so weak and exhausted he could barely smile. Three or four times a week he was wheeled on a trolley from his hospital bed to become entangled in the sinister mysteries of Ward Five. I would arrive, usually a good half hour before his treatment was over, to accompany him back to the ward and what, by comparison, was normality.

The dialysis unit was a modern, purpose-built, flat-roofed, soulless building with huge, steel-framed curtainless windows covered by slatted blinds to thwart prying eyes. Inside, cold, hard, moulded-plastic chairs stood on dark, polished linoleum against stark and unfriendly walls. A thick red line painted on the floor separated the reception area from the dialysis unit and the warm, loving relatives from the sad, sick patients within. A large blackboard, on which were written the names of all the dialysis patients, stood on an easel beside a sign saying curtly 'No admittance beyond this point'. Any relative venturing this far would be able to recognize the name of his loved one prefacing a long line of unintelligible tags and signs denoting the patient's condition and progress: dry weight; weight gain between dialyses; weight loss; blood pressure; pulse; and temperature, all underlying the seriousness of the situation. What went on behind those closed swing-doors, what rituals and incantations? Certainly, at that time, Timbo could not enlighten me and no one else cared enough to want to try.

There were to be many weeks before we took him home, my training period behind me, to plunge head first into the deep, dark waters of home dialysis. In the meantime I waited patiently, terrified, for the remains of my son to be handed over on his trolley for the push back to the ward and his hospital bed.

There is in all of us a natural instinct to cling to something solid when the waters get too rough, to save ourselves from drowning. I found my salvation in the most solid member of the dialysis team, Doug Farrend, and clung to him for all my worth. A short, stocky man of middle age, straight as a die, with no nonsense about him, he was the one strong, unsinkable ship in a sea of wrecks and flotsam. A retired 'sparky' who had served a full term in the Royal Navy, he had been appointed chief technician to the unit. A tough task-master when it came to learning the intricacies of dialysis, he was at the same time a man of great human understanding, with deep compassion. I remember well one evening standing by the trolley looking down on the still figure of my recumbent son and watching the tears well from beneath his closed lids and course silently down his cheeks. Not a word of complaint or self-pity, just a quiet plea that he had had enough. I looked across at Doug, who was standing at the trolley's head; no doubt something in the expression on my face caused him to react immediately.

'Come, come now. We mustn't look gloomy. We are only pulling all this fluid weight off him so that we can build him up and start again.'

'Build him up and start again.' Such words of hope and purpose denied the possibility of defeat and gave me strength during the weeks ahead.

The first time I saw Timbo on dialysis was at the start of my training for the home programme and my reaction was extra-ordinary. The sight of him lying there on the bed with two blood-filled tubes appearing from his left leg and dis-appearing in the direction of a huge, noisy, rattling machine filled me with embarrassment. I felt as I would had I chanced upon a couple making love, or pushed open an unlocked bathroom door in all innocence, revealing a stranger relaxed in the knowledge of his privacy. Yet Timbo was thrilled to have me with him and explained the workings of the machine with all the fervour of an eight year old showing off with pride his first train set. But the fact that he was attached to that machine and it to him, his life's blood flowing through yards of tubes pumping carelessly on the floor at the beat of his own heart, was something too awful for me to comprehend and I could only marvel at his amazing spirit and acceptance of his lot, whilst I covered my shame with magpie chatterings. The training sessions under Doug's kindly bullying went well, and I passed with flying colours just three weeks from the start. Doug, I am sure, was as confident of my competence as I was certain of my lack of it, but my one aim was to get Timbo home and away from hospital and somehow, with him to help me, we would manage. He was having his last dialysis in hospital prior to his first at home when all the equipment, disposables, and the rest of the paraphernalia arrived. He had made me promise that I would not open anything until he came home, as if it were Christmas time and the parcels on the tree were all addressed to him. 'Oh look Mum, we've got a bucket and fourteen forceps and all these syringes and where are we going to put...'.... the coils, lines, rubber gloves, and masks. He carefully labelled the buckets and the bins 'dirty only' and 'clean only' with such enthusiasm and delight that I really began to think that perhaps Christmas had come after all!

Once he was home my task was to prepare the machine ready for him on his return from the daily crammer he was attending in the vain hope of picking up some more 'O' levels. I would hear his car come up the drive, listen for the engine to be switched off, and count his footsteps as they passed under the window where I was preparing his machine, shaking from head to foot. I just could not get a grip on myself, could not control the awful anxiety stemming from the instilled knowledge that I must do everything right because one small slip might prove fatal. He would pop his head into the dialysis room with a cheery greeting, and with a 'tell me when you are ready for me, Mum' would go down the stairs to watch some favourite programme, leaving me to continue with the preparation of his machine. Whilst in some ways his carefree attitude towards his treatment gave me confidence, in other ways it was harder for me because I did not feel that he was sharing the responsibility. I would stand by his bed watching nervously as he connected his blood lines to the shunt in his leg, waiting for that moment when he would remove the clips and with a gush the blood would begin to flow through the lines. He would be prattling on about the events of the day, apparently unaware of the implications of what he was doing, whilst I would be silently praying that once again all would go well and repeating over and over again the unspoken words, 'Oh Timbo, concentrate, do concentrate!'

I was very anxious for all our sakes that life should continue as near normal as possible. I have never played tennis better than that summer as, in order to hit the ball at all, I had to clear my mind of all its pressures and involve myself one hundred per cent with what I was doing. Off the tennis court I found this almost impossible, but I certainly tried. I even invited people to dinner on dialysis nights, bringing our half of the intercom, normally in our bedroom, down the stairs to the drawing-room so that I could be alerted to any alarms and keep in touch with Timbo should he need me unexpectedly. But as a hostess I know I was a failure and in the end dialysis nights and, later, days were given over to the machine.

# 3

# The Promise of a New Life

In those relatively early days of dialysis little was known about the effect of such rigorous and debilitating treatment on the body, and twelve hours twice a week was the rule at Portsmouth. Timbo found it impossible to stick to his limited fluid intake so consequently he was always overloaded and great was my concern and his disappointment when the doctors told us that he must dialyse for nine hours three times a week. We saw it as a punishment for his dietary indiscretions rather than as a medical necessity. He dialysed at night for the first year and whilst I had cause too often to ring our local doctor in the small hours of the morning, it was more from the need for the strength given by kindly medical support than from a fear of imminent disaster. Recognizing the urgency in my voice, he would pull on his trousers over his pyjama bottoms, throw a coat over the top, and dash through the night to be at Timbo's bedside within minutes.

I remember well the Portsmouth renal doctor, perhaps realizing that the strain was beginning to tell, saying to me: 'When his treatment is over, close the treatment room door and forget about it until the next time.'! The words, no doubt, were meant well but showed such utter lack of understanding and imagination that they served only to widen the gap between doctor and relative. Timbo was usually on the machine by 9.00 p.m. and off by 6.00 a.m. During the first four hours he was allowed to eat anything he liked, within reason, and my joy was to cook him his evening meal. Something simple like sausages and chips, or baked beans on fried bread, or spaghetti bolognese – all foods forbidden to him at other times. He slept through most of the night, no doubt waking from time to time, and I dozed fitfully until morning with the intercom beside me. As soon as he was off the machine he went back to his own room for two hours' sleep whilst I cleared up the treatment room.

One early morning after a particularly bad night, with the machine alarming constantly, and Timbo being sick at intervals and in fearful pain from cramp, I was feeling particularly low. The door of the dialysis room opened and a voice said, 'Does anybody want any help in here?' With tousled head and bleary eyes, his old, blue-towelling dressing-gown wrapped around him, Nigel stood in the open doorway. Just an ordinary man offering his much-needed help, but to me he could have been God himself. From then on Nigel and I became a dialysis team and as Timbo became more ill and more dilapidated I was grateful beyond words to have his support.

At about the time of the onset of Timbo's illness I was walking through a London park one early morning. Coming towards me was a young man in his early twenties, head held high, back straight, left arm swinging, and in his right hand he held the stiff white harness of a guide-dog. Hearing my advancing footsteps he stopped before me and asked for directions as to the best and safest place to cross Park Lane. I stood and watched him striding out with fearless confidence towards the crossing of my choice and thought how wonderful it was that this young man could keep his independence, walk tall, and pull his weight in the community despite his disability, and I vowed then and there that one day I would make time to support this worthy cause. I kept my promise to myself and for a few years prior to Timbo's entry into the world of dialysis and transplantation I had been raising money for the Guide Dogs for the Blind. My experience was limited but my efforts not unsuccessful, so when in 1971 I dedicated myself to the plight of kidney patients in this country I was not entirely a raw recruit to the world of fund raising.

It was about that time that I also began to have thoughts for the mothers of other sick children and wondered how they fared. 'Don't forget his high protein diet. Plenty of steak, chicken, eggs, and fish; cream is good for him, so make sure he has that too,' were the words I had often heard at the end of clinic. How on earth could these simple instructions possibly be carried out by wives of men earning a modest wage? How in heaven's name did other mothers cope with the endless demands made by their sick children forced to lie in hospital – more Lucozade, crayons, colouring books, a favourite comic. No mother can go empty-handed to visit her child in hospital, and how the cost mounts up.

During two long years, between 1970 and 1972, whilst Timbo and I were struggling with home dialysis I worked hard in my own small way to raise money for kidney research. Being the mother of a patient attending St Mary's Hospital, Portsmouth, I was not encouraged to seek the companionship of other relatives – in fact, relatives were not encouraged at all! So although I had some idea of the enormous financial burden under which so many of the renal families were struggling I didn't know enough and, anxious to appease my gods, the renal physicians, I turned my attention to raising money for renal research.

I was wise enough to appreciate the need for credibility and persuaded the then Director of the National Kidney Research Fund (NKRF) to allow me to use their notepaper and to fund raise in their name. In 1971 I had printed the first of many annual brochures entitled 'The Silver Lining Appeal of the National Kidney Research Fund'. At the bottom of the cover were the words 'All proceeds to Guy's Hospital, London and St Mary's Hospital, Portsmouth'.

There is very strong feeling amongst fund-raising relatives that somehow the money raised and handed to the patient's

consultant will ensure better and kinder treatment and a
longer life for the patient. Not having received the first, and
anxious to ensure the second, I threw all the energy I had left
after the rigours of dialysis into raising funds for those two
hospitals. To one I was saying 'thank you' and to the other
'please'. Since the Articles of Association of the NKRF, to
whom I had affiliated myself, stated quite clearly that all
monies raised on their behalf were to be used for the purpose
of research, there was much consternation shown at my
insistence that the money raised by me should be sent direct,
without strings attached, to the two recipients mentioned. It
is amazing to me now that the Director of the charity, and the
Medical Committee, suffered my arrogance but I can only
suppose that they realized my worth in a practical way and
had not yet appreciated that they had caught a tiger by the
tail.

I ran fund-raising events, wrote endless pleas for help, and
found to my gratification that being the mother of a kidney
patient – immersed as I was, up to my neck, in the horrors of
dialysis, understanding so well the frustrations and limitations of the parents' lives – help was forthcoming in a way
that I had never dared to hope. Running alongside my understanding of the need for financial support for the hospitals
caring for these renal patients was the awareness that
hundreds of dialysis patients like Timbo, with their lives in
ruins about them, waited with brave hope for the chance to
live a normal life through transplantation and were being
needlessly denied this chance as hundreds of viable kidneys
were burned in crematoria and buried in graveyards every
day, and no one seemed to care.

Timbo's illness had become the pivot of my life and certainly
at that time his life revolved around the excitement of being
young and the challenge of youthful things. Neither his father
nor his mother will ever accept responsibility for the
introduction of the idea that his unfortunate situation
warranted occasional spoiling. So when one of us, drunk with

relief at his release from hospital, popped the hackneyed question, 'What would you like more than anything else in the world, darling?' he replied without hesitation, 'A Lotus Elan!' He had passed his driving test only three days after his seventeenth birthday so that by the time he was discharged from hospital he was an old hand, with all of thirty hours ungrazed experience to his credit! Lotus were offering six free flying lessons in a Piper Cherokee to every buyer during the months of August and September so, in addition to the doubtful pleasure of being driven by my inexperienced son on his weekly visits to Blackbush Aerodrome, was the hair-raising experience of watching him disappear into the misty distance at the end of the runway. I was quite clear in my own mind which of the two experiences I preferred and, relaxing in the long grass at the edge of the airfield awaiting his return, I only questioned that so much dedication had gone into his preservation when undoubtedly he was to die not on a kidney machine, but on the road or in the air!

After five lessons he was already flying the machine himself with his instructor sitting behind him, when his renal physician at Portsmouth came to hear of his enterprising exploits. A letter arrived on the breakfast table shortly before his final lesson. His doctor wrote that as he was still very anaemic and might lose consciousness in certain conditions such as those that could easily arise while flying, we should delay flying lessons until later. He added that Timbo should also avoid driving his car on any day when he didn't feel entirely well, all of which made me grateful that our flying time together had nearly come to an end.

We were determined that things should continue without too much interruption and I devoted much of my time to ensuring that the life that Timbo had enjoyed before the need for dialysis was not gone for ever. One of his bitter dis-appointments was the realization that both swimming and skiing must become joys of the past because of the shunt in his leg and the fear of damage and infection. I spent many enjoyable hours setting my mind to the problem of how to

devise a foolproof leg protector, and with the enthusiastic
cooperation of a company concerned with plastics we
produced a sturdy leg shield, which was not only waterproof
but could also withstand a kick from a mule without denting.
It was specially fitted to his own leg but, sadly, by the time it
was completed and ready to wear, he was in no fit state to
consider either of the activities for which it was intended.

He was as full of schemes for himself as I was for him, and
whilst I did not go along with his wish to join a parachuting
club, at least I went along with it far enough to make tentative
enquiries of the doctors at Guy's as to the suitability of such a
plan for a young man in his physical condition. My enquiry
was treated with amusement and disbelief and I was assured
that, with Timbo's bones in the condition they were in, the
chances of his progressing past the first lesson were minimal!
With relief I was able to pass on to Timbo the view of the
doctors that the first practice fall off the back of the lorry
would doubtless produce multiple fractures, so we set our
minds to more practical schemes.

His sense of humour which, amazingly enough, has never
deserted him, was always there to keep us from taking life too
seriously. Returning from hospital at the end of a particularly
difficult week when he had been admitted with innumerable
complications, there had been talk of the possibility that I
might be able to give him one of my kidneys in a transplant
operation.

'Well,' he said, after some thought. 'I hope they give it a
jolly good squeeze first, that's all I can say, because I would
like to feel that the first time I pee it's mine, not yours!'

I remember on one occasion, when his shunt needed
revision, we drove down to Portsmouth keeping our spirits
high by composing alternative verses to the Christmas Carol
'While Shepherds watch their Flocks by Night'. Shepherd
was the name of the surgeon at St Mary's in charge of shunt
making, but apart from the initial line 'Whilst Shepherd fixes
Shunts at Night' the rest of the verses escape me now and,
whilst I am sure they would not have been worthy of

recording, they did take our minds off the horrors ahead and the car was filled with much genuine laughter. On arrival at the hospital I sat on a chair beside the trolley on which Timbo lay, awaiting his pre-med in an empty sideward. It was quite late in the evening and the surgeon had been called back to the hospital for what was a minor emergency. We waited together, chatting idly, Timbo getting apparently more and more drowsy, when the door opened and the surgeon appeared. Dressed from head to foot in green, including green gumboots, he certainly looked the part, and with a friendly nod in my direction he put his hands to the back of Timbo's trolley and proceeded to push him in the direction of the theatre. I was most surprised by the strength in Timbo's voice pleading with the surgeon to allow me to accompany him! I had no desire whatsoever to watch the knife being thrust into my son's leg, but if Timbo wanted me to be there then, if I could, I would be. The surgeon looked doubtful at this unusual request but with no nursing staff around he was obviously prepared to give the request his serious consideration.

'Are you sure you won't faint at the sight of his blood?' he asked me dubiously, and before I had a chance to assure him that I had never fainted in my life, Timbo's voice from the trolley saying, 'Don't be silly. She was a VAD [Voluntary Aid Detachment] in the War!' clinched it, and I followed the surgeon into the theatre.

Timbo was given what must have been a strong local anaesthetic and I sat by his head, surreptitiously holding his hand under the blanket and keeping as far away from the scene of action as was physically possible. The surgeon, sitting comfortably on a stool beside Timbo's left leg humming to himself in a preoccupied way, lifted the scalpel and I turned my head away. He must have thought I was an unusual mother since he lifted his head and, looking in my direction, said, 'You can't see properly over there, can you? Bring your chair nearer and I'll explain what I am doing.'

I sat transfixed as he pulled out Timbo's veins from a large, deep wound in the side of his leg and inspected each one thoughtfully. I tried to look suitably interested and to disassociate the gory hole before me from the leg of my son. Timbo was obviously pleased to have me with him and no doubt thought I was fascinated by the sight before my eyes. When it was over he was bandaged up by the surgeon himself, and we drove home together quite late at night filling the car with a new set of verses.

With Timbo established on home dialysis and my daily trips to Portsmouth temporarily behind me, I set about joining the system I was quite unable to beat. We had been told that Timbo would be put on the transplant list and that a kidney could be found for him at any time. 'Keep a case packed, the car full of petrol, and be ready to leave at any moment for Guy's when the call comes,' were the instructions. It was to be more than two years before the call came from the hospital. 'Come as quickly as you can. We have a kidney for him.' Mingled with apprehension was relief and thankfulness.

By the summer of 1971, while waiting for the donor kidney, my impatience and indignation had reached boiling-point. Not one column-inch in a whole year had been devoted by the national press to the plight of dialysis patients waiting for a suitable cadaver kidney to give them new life. With the idea of getting the attention of the national press, not of finding a suitable kidney for Timbo, I placed an advertisement in the 'Personal' column of *The Times* which read: 'B.A. *B.T. 15. 12. Group A – A donated cadaver kidney of this tissue type will release an eighteen year old from the wretchedness of his machine. Please help – Bordon 2021.' By 11 o'clock on Thursday 26 August no fewer than eleven national dailies had contacted me on the telephone wanting to know the meaning of the advertisement. It was my chance to tell the story as I saw it, and I made full use of the opportunity. The next day was mini Budget Day and our story took only second place to the news that every Englishman was waiting to hear.

'Anxious mum places "ad" for kidney' said the *Daily Express*; 'Please give my boy a kidney, says ad from a mother' wrote the *Daily Mirror*; 'Give my son a new life, pleads mother' were the headlines in the *Daily Mail*, and so on.

At long last the story had been told and in my innocence and naïvety I thought that it would be the end of anxious waiting for all Britain's dialysis patients and those that loved them. It was, in fact, to be no more than the start of an endless campaign that I have run ever since. I have at least created awareness, so that there can now be no man or woman left in this country who does not know of the need for kidney donation, but despite all my efforts and caring and understanding, I can say with bitterness that little else has been achieved.

During that time I had been writing regularly to Sir Keith Joseph, who was then the Secretary of State for Health. I sent him an example of a kidney donor card which I had received from a friend in the States, begging him to allow its introduction into this country. I had always received a reply, not only prompt and courteous, but signed by himself. In reply to one of my more impassioned pleas, I received a letter with these words: 'We do not feel the climate is right to introduce the donor card at this stage.'

I wrote back to him at once, acknowledging the fact that I was hitting below the belt. 'Your son James and my son Timothy were at Harrow together. Had it been James who had had to leave school early, with his life in ruins about him, I do not think that you would be concerned with whether or not the climate was right. I know you would be moving heaven and earth to help him. Sadly it is Timothy struggling for his existence on thrice-weekly dialysis, not James, since you are in a position to help, but I can do nothing.'

Two or three weeks went by I remember before I received a reply. Sir Keith wrote that he had good news for me and invited me to attend a meeting at the Department of Health and Social Security at the Elephant and Castle where senior civil servants involved with kidney patients would discuss with me the introduction of a Government Kidney Donor Scheme.

Determined not to lose an inch of the progress made, I went to the meeting equipped with a large mock-up of my first poster in artwork form. Since available funds were nil, I had found a photographer prepared to work without charge in return for a commission from the *Sunday Telegraph Colour Supplement*, who were planning a profile of me. I had two willing models in the shape of my impecunious, underfed nursing daughter and the medical student son of our local GP, who offered themselves in return for a free meal, while a sympathetic friend working with a top London advertising agency did the artwork during one week-end for love. The words on the poster, 'Harry Morgan left a fob-watch to his son, an insurance policy to his wife, and something very special to two perfect strangers', came chiefly from myself.

At the meeting we sat around a long table together whilst those present studied and discussed the artwork. I was excited and enthusiastic, and confident that they would not be able to resist the obvious attraction of the poster before them. What would be the point of introducing the donor card – and that hurdle, I learnt, had already been leapt – if there were no accompanying publicity? They agreed, finally, that the poster looked good. The conversation moved on from the general to the particular. How many posters should be printed? Who would be responsible for their distribution? Whose advertising agency would be printing them – theirs or mine?

It was at this point that one of the brighter boys looked straight at me and said, 'Right, but who's paying for all of this anyway?'

'You are, of course,' I replied. 'Surely this is your kidney donor scheme?'

So it was that the Government's Kidney Donor Scheme came into being. By the time of our first transplant call the donor cards had been slipped onto a disinterested, reluctant market with no fanfare of trumpets to introduce in my view one of the most important government schemes of the day.

Our dash to London, car hazard lights flashing, and our hearts thumping, was to be the first of several false alarms. On arrival at Guy's Hospital we were given the news that, at the last minute, the relatives had changed their minds and decided not to allow the kidney to be used for the saving of two other lives. It is not hard to imagine how difficult it was for us all to go back to the old routine and believe that one day there would be freedom from the fearful rigours, limitations, and frustrations of life on a kidney machine. It took a great deal of courage to face such bitter disappointment, but courage was something Timbo never lacked.

In those months before his first transplant I threw myself whole-heartedly into chasing down every possible avenue which might lead to the availability of more donor kidneys for transplantation. I pushed myself immodestly in front of television programme producers, women's magazine editors, and the national daily press. I made my debut on 'Woman's Hour', tackled Members of Parliament, and slowly but surely, bit by bit, I made a little ground.

I was to live through two and a half long years, several operations and much agony before his first transplant call came. Monday, 20 March 1972 was, unbeknown to me, to be the date of his last dialysis at home. It had been a particularly bad session: he had become so ill and had deteriorated so much in body and spirit that we were no longer dialysing at night. I had turned my back on him and was standing silently at the window with tears coursing down my cheeks, trying to shut my ears to his cries and pleadings. He had been begging me to take him off the machine before the allocated time; nine hours was the time prescribed, and only seven had passed – seven hours of agonizing cramps with every part of his wretched body twisted and knotted in spasm. I think both of us knew that we couldn't continue much longer. How hard I prayed that that dialysis would be the last!

By the time Timbo was successfully transplanted for the

first time on 21 March 1972 I had spread the word as far as I knew how. All my concentration was on the shortage of donor kidneys for transplantation and the poor distribution of the donor cards. I persuaded a number of companies and organizations to use their outlets as distribution points; petrol companies carried cards briefly on the forecourts of their petrol stations; supermarkets had them for a short time on their check-out points; and an occasional editor was willing to enlose one card in several thousand copies of his magazine. My most exciting achievement at that time was to bully the Committee of the Pharmaceutical Society into agreeing that all members should receive a circular urging them to display the donor cards in their chemist shops, but sadly this came to nothing. Whilst it was obvious to me that a chemist shop, of all places, should have donor cards available to their customers, even I could see their shelf space was limited. I also approached the then Defence Minister, William Rodgers, and begged him to ensure that donor cards were carried by members of the Armed Forces. I was assured that he would give serious consideration to my plea, but it was rejected on the grounds that there might be repercussions from the mother of a son newly sent to Northern Ireland because of the implications of the carrying of a donor card. What about the mothers of those kidney patients wasting their lives away on kidney machines, many of them dying before a suitable kidney could be found for them?

Timbo's first transplant was a miracle to us. Only ten days after the operation he was home again sharing Easter with us, stuffing himself with chocolate, a forbidden treat for dialysis patients, drinking whatever he liked and as much as he liked, and our joy was unbounded. He was nineteen years old and suddenly the door of his prison cell had opened and the light streamed through. He joined his elder sister, Susie, in her London flat and began his working life at Sotheby's, the fine art auctioneers in Bond Street. My diary of that period shows that, apart from a few agonizing times when he was re-admitted to hospital for investigation or surgery connected with the suspected rejection of the kidney, we lived in comparative peace until February 1973.

When Timbo headed for London that April evening in 1972, only three weeks after his first transplant, I hardly expected to see him again except for when he joined us all for the family Christmas. For years he had been forced into a close, unnatural alliance with his mother, so who could have blamed him if, despite loving me as, I am sure he did, he could not wait to put the miles and months between us? He had been the very essence of my being for so long that part of me dreaded the emptiness that his going would leave, but I knew how vital it was that I should give him his freedom and place his destiny firmly in his own hands. The crunch of the car wheels on the drive had scarcely faded – unlike the brave smile on my face – when the telephone rang. It was Timbo's transplant surgeon, Mick Bewick.

'I'm afraid Timbo has just left for London,' I said.

'I know,' was the reply. 'I didn't ring to speak to him, I rang to speak to you. I thought you might be feeling lonely.'

I'm afraid that his kindness and understanding were too much for me and I repaid him by bursting into tears.

In fact, surprisingly enough, Timbo was to choose only one week-end away from home for the next ten months, so in February 1973 he was with us when the lump appeared. A small swelling beneath the transplant scar showed itself one morning at breakfast. By lunch-time it had at least doubled in size, and in the early afternoon he drove himself to Guy's hospital. The surgeon thought that it was a stitch abscess, lanced it, and sent him back to his flat. He rang me later that evening to tell me that colourless fluid had been pouring from the hole the surgeon made for several hours, and that his clothes were soaked.

'It looks like water,' he said.

I tried to keep my voice steady when I asked, 'Do you think, darling, it could be urine?'

The thought was both too horrible and too obvious. He returned to Guy's in a taxi, the lower part of his waist swathed in a bath towel, and I sat at home fearing the worst. The ureter had parted from the kidney and the urine was bypassing his bladder and coming out of the hole in his side. More surgery, and then infection set in, and it was many weeks before he left the hospital.

I have vivid memories of those weeks and can feel again the fear, the horror, and the utter helplessness. I travelled up to London by train each morning, arriving at the hospital at 9.00 a.m. I collected the mail from the local Post Office on my way to the station and did my best to read, with intelligence and interest, some of the many letters connected with my work that had started arriving at home. I prayed, and read a little, and prayed again that when I arrived at the hospital I would find Timbo no worse than the evening before. Usually the problem of yesterday had been superseded by a new and even greater problem. I used very often to walk up the stairs to the fourth floor rather than take the lift, in order to postpone the time when I would have to take hold of myself and prepare myself to hear the worst. I always rang his ward before leaving for the station to make quite sure that he had not died in the night.

It was always gratifying when the evenings came to see the number of new friends he had made during his months of freedom. Young people like himself and some, of course, older; people who really cared and gave up hours of their own free time to sit by his bed and chat with one another, letting him know that they were rooting for him. It also gave me a chance to talk in a gay, light-hearted way, which helped me to blot out the sights and sounds of what went on around me. Timbo was always resentful that I seemed to pay so little heed to him. 'I don't know why you bother to come when you only ask questions about the other patients and talk to them,' he often said. How could he have understood that the only way that I could cope was to concentrate my mind on the problems of the others?

I remember so well sitting beside his bed one afternoon and noticing blood seeping from his wound through the dressing and the stark white sheet. The nurses had changed the dressing frequently in order to try and staunch the flow and it had seemed that all was well. I don't know what it is about the sight of the blood of those we love that fills us so with horror. I called his attention to the widening stain but he was unconcerned and once again I drew comfort from him. When I was at his side I got reassurance from the fact that whilst terrible changes were taking place to his body, his spirit was quite unchanged and I knew he would survive. It was only when I was parted from him each night that cold fear gripped me every time the telphone rang.

For five long weeks I made the daily trip to Guy's and at the week-ends Nigel would come too, and sit in the day-room watching football on the television. Occasionally he would bring the car up in the evening after work during the week and we would drive home together in black despair. Nigel found in his work, as I did, a retreat from the bleak realities of life.

The doctors decided that I had had enough and urged me to accompany Nigel on a short business trip to Sweden, leaving Timbo for four days. I had to be almost literally prised from my place beside his hospital bed, but I realized, too, that I owed it to Nigel to give a little of myself to him. I rang the hospital daily for news, which was always good, but I was left too long alone whilst Nigel was in conference and I roamed the Swedish streets fretting and yearning to be back with Timbo. On our return to Harwich we drove straight to Guy's and we were told we could take him home. Driving back in the car to Hampshire and sitting in the front seat for comfort, Timbo put his hands above his head and taking mine he said, 'I began to think I would never see you again. How good it is to be going home.'

# 4

# The Plan is Laid

During that year of 1973 I continued my fund-raising activities and campaigning for more cadaver kidneys for transplantation. Timbo, who was still working at Sotheby's when his health allowed, assured me of the charitable attitude of the company's directors and gave me the idea for a new way of raising money.

I had already experienced a windfall in my first introduction to the salerooms in the shape of a small blue Meissen jug, which had been given to me by a supportive peer in the mistaken belief that it would fetch around £40 for my cause. This kind and considerate man, anxious to help in the most practical way possible, had sent me 'a little blue jug' with the instructions that I was to be sure to let him know if it did not make his estimated value as he would like to make up the shortfall. Timbo, who was with me when the jug was unwrapped, recognized it immediately for what it was worth and came with me to the porcelain sale at Sotheby's in which it had been entered. Being the sort of son who always admired outrageous hats on other mothers but preferred his own mother to blend into the background, and being myself the sort of person who has almost fallen out of boxes at the races with excitement when my horse comes in, I found it hard to contain my enthusiasm when the bidding went past £40 to £100, £150, £200, £250, and so on until the magnificent sum of £1,250 had been called and the hammer fell for the third time.

Fortunately my memory has practically erased the scenes of my unseemly and vocal jubilation but I was certainly encouraged to try and get together suitable items for a charity sale.

My first sale was held that year at Bonham's, the firm of fine art auctioneers in Montpelier Street. A family firm of the old style run by two delightful people, Leonard and Diana Bonham, whom I had known for many years. Feeling it unlikely that I was sufficiently worthy a cause to attract gifts of beautiful paintings, I decided to place myself in the generous hands of both dealer and buyer. I approached the directors of many of the London galleries and asked for a contribution to my forthcoming sale, not in the form of an outright gift, but in return for a considerably smaller profit margin than that they would normally make, the rest of the profit going to my fund. It was then up to the buyers to show their generosity and at the same time to appreciate that they had the opportunity of buying a bargain. The idea was well received by the dealers and the buyers excelled themselves in their support. Since the pictures were given to me on a sale or return basis, no capital was involved and the normal profit margin that the galleries would expect to make was sufficient to ensure a healthy return to the fund as well as a bargain for the buyer. Bonham's generously waived their normal commission and the sale was a great success, and enormous fun. It offered me the opportunity of explaining the needs and problems of the kidney patients to a different circle of friends.

When eventually I did manage to gather together an incredible assortment of items for a sale at Sotheby's it was not until October 1980.

In those early days I was working entirely alone, organizing the fund-raising events which were my only source of charity income. No expenses were taken from the monies raised and Nigel, with growing concern, found himself paying for all.

The previous year I had conceived the idea of a carol concert at the beautiful church of St Peter's, Eaton Square. I had had the good fortune to meet the vicar at the house of a friend during preparations for her daughter's wedding (sadly the vicar has since changed), and he was a kindly, caring, enthusiastic fellow with a mind open to new ideas if they supported his own view of Christianity. He was delighted to make his church available to me free of charge and I threw myself with enormous energy and dedication into the exciting task of inviting and securing personalities from the stage and the political arena, who would enthrall us with readings of their choice, and vocalists of reputation and renown with beautiful voices to inspire us. I wrote without hesitation or any thought of being refused to those people who, in my understanding, were top of their professions. A business acquaintance of ours was director of the St Albans Chamber Choir and I persuaded him, without much difficulty, to coach the choir all the way to Eaton Square in return for my grateful thanks and tea and biscuits in the vestry. They sang beautifully and, during the eight years of my carol concerts, received the accolade from such notable musicians as Edward Heath, Dame Janet Baker, André Previn, and their like, so hopefully they were well rewarded for their kindness. Our expenses were nil since even the little leaflets announcing the concert were printed free of charge by a friend of mine, and in those early years I personally walked many street miles placing the leaflets through letterboxes, on club notice-boards, in local schools, and, as a last resort, beneath the windscreen wipers of those cars parked in the vicinity sporting a residents parking permit! The price of the tickets that first year, I remember, was 60p – a small price to pay for the joy of hearing the singing of Ileana Cotrubas, Derek Hammond-Stroud, and Dame Janet Baker, and of listening to the readings of such great actors as Edward Fox, Daniel Massey, Kenneth More, and Robert Morley.

In all the years that I ran these concerts I never had any difficulty in attracting stars and personalities, but for them to give up their precious time for so small a return to the charity they were supporting seemed, in the end, too much for me to ask. Whilst the choir continued to seem well-satisfied with their tea and biscuits in the vestry, I laid on a small reception of thanks for those taking part. I was a member of the Institute of Director's Club, conveniently situated at that time in Belgrave Square just behind the church. With the exception of the drink, for which we were charged at cost, the kind and caring Director-General and the Banqueting Manager, who incredibly enough in later years was to become a dialysis patient himself, allowed me to use the beautiful drawing-room there free of charge and the cocktail canapés were supplied and paid for by the staff.

In the year that Edward Heath accepted my invitation he was Prime Minister and fighting a fearful battle with the miners. He had already cancelled his visit to Broadstairs where he annually conducted the choir at the carol concert there. My friends all said it was unrealistic of me to hope that he would come to my concert when he had already cancelled his own, but I knew that he would and he did.

Coming down the aisle together, I could see through the open doors his chauffeur-driven car awaiting him. Since mine was parked some way away from the church, I realized in one awful moment that the Prime Minister was going to arrive at my reception before I did myself Such was the case and, on my arrival, I found him glass in hand happily chatting with his detective.

The following year when Angus Ogilvy was my guest of honour, I readily accepted his invitation of a lift so that we arrived at the reception together. I remember well his turning to me and asking, 'How on earth do you manage to get such important people to come?'

'But you are one of them,' I replied. 'Why did you come?'

He told me that he had thought what I was doing was a good thing, but he was still intrigued to know why the others had accepted my invitation, so later on during the course of the reception we went round asking them! Sir Geoffrey Howe, David Attenborough, Josephine Barstow, Clement Freud, and others, were all confronted with this question and the answer was the same. I was well pleased.

Meanwhile, one of the aspects of the kidney donor card which did concern me was the apparent necessity for the written permission of the next of kin before the wishes of the donor could be carried out. I had a meeting with Barbara Castle, who at that time was Secretary of State for Health, and the Minister, Dr David Owen, and told them that following a recent radio broadcast when I was given the opportunity of appealing for kidney donors and discussing the need for them, I had received an alarming number of letters from listeners, mostly women, whose husbands had refused to sign their cards, thus depriving them of the opportunity of becoming a kidney donor.

Mrs Castle was genuinely horrified and holding the current donor car in her hand she turned to Dr Owen and said, 'Do you mean to tell me, David, that if I was to sign this card saying that I wanted my kidneys to be used to save the lives of two other people after my death, that Ted could refuse to allow them to be taken?'

To Dr Owen's affirmative, she replied, 'I think this is scandalous. The wishes of the donor should be paramount,' and turning to one of the quivering Civil Servants, who had apparently only recently reordered a further two million of the current cards, she said, 'This must be changed immediately: the permission of the next of kin is not a legal requirement and people should be allowed to donate their kidneys if they wish without fear of their wishes being denied.'

I remember the look of extreme disbelief, mingled with horror, on the face of the Civil Servant who told me afterwards, as we were walking down the corridor together to the lift, that certainly for some months to come there was no question of the donor card being changed. That meeting was an eye-opener for me, since up to that time I had vastly underestimated the power of the senior Civil Servant.

The New Year of 1974 saw three special family occasions. On 3 January Timbo celebrated his twenty-first birthday, a year we had never expected him to reach. We took over the restaurant at the Norwegian Centre in Knightsbridge for the evening, and surrounded by his family and friends and those doctors whose skill and devotion had enabled him to reach maturity, we celebrated as never before. Timbo, looking well and happy, stood up to make a brief speech of welcome and opened out his arms as if embracing all of us who with our love and support had, in our different ways, helped him through four difficult years. My heart was overflowing and my happiness knew no bounds. Two days later his elder sister, Susie, who had by that time been called to the Bar, was married at the Temple Church, her younger sister a proud and lovely bridesmaid and Timbo doing energetic duties as an usher. The family celebrations that winter culminated in Nigel's fiftieth birthday only six days later. Such an auspicious start to the year gave no room for feelings of gloom or preparation for the disappointment and horror that lay ahead.

With the idea of filling each unforgiving minute and widening my area of involvement, I had eagerly accepted an invitation to become a Justice of the Peace in early 1974. My family and friends told me that I was crazy to even consider taking on anything in addition to my work for kidney patients, but I had always been interested in both the law and the law-breakers and took up my new work with enthusiasm. Since at that time my work for kidney patients had not grown to the enormous proportions that it has today, it seemed to me that I could without trouble devote one day a week to the process of the law. I enjoyed the work immensely, found it both interesting and satisfying, and for the first few years looked forward greatly to Friday mornings and my trip to the Court, where I was able to cast my mind over a variety of problems, none of them remotely connected with renal disease. As the pressure of my work in the office continued to increase, however, there came a time when I felt I was not giving my full mind and dedication to my work as a Magistrate. I continued, of course, to turn up on Fridays but often was not able to remain after lunch because of my other commitments and I was conscious of placing an unfair burden on my colleagues. In the autumn of 1982, after only eight and a half years on the bench, I reluctantly handed in my resignation – and my friends and family then thought I was as crazy to give up the job as they had first felt I had been to take it on!

At the beginning of February Timbo's health was the best it had been for many months and with his grafted kidney approaching its second birthday he decided not to wait until the summer for a much-needed and longed-for break. It was four years since he had last had a holiday and he was disappointed to find that the first available date for his planned trip with a friend to the Caribbean was on 2 May. Sadly, that date found him once more lying in a hospital bed whilst the doctors fought without success to save the kidney. On 3 May, our wedding anniversary, they took the kidney out and he was once more back on a kidney machine. My memories of that time are very vivid but they paint pictures not of Timbo's bitter disappointment and loss of freedom, nor of his pain and anguish, but of my own indignant anger at the fearful turn of events.

Timbo had been a home dialysis patient, looked after like many hundreds of other kidney patients in this country both then and today by a loving relative. When, at the age of nineteen, he was first transplanted he naturally moved away from home to lead a young life in London where he worked. Two years later, when his transplant failed, he was sharing a flat with three other young people and no way could it have been right or fair to have expected him to return once more to his country home. If his spirit was to survive and if he was to have a chance of holding on to his job at Sotheby's it was imperative that he was dialysed in London – but where? Guy's Hospital, where he had been looked after for so many years, had adopted a policy whereby no patient could be taken on to the dialysis programme unless either he could be transplanted in a matter of months or he could be treated at home. Rules, in my opinion, are made to be broken and it is exceptions that prove them, but in Timbo's case there were to be no exceptions and the head of the department was adamant. Timbo could not be dialysed in the chronic and overcrowded situation at Guy's Hospital renal unit.

My anger and despair were only matched by my disbelief that these doctors who had, as it were, held his hand through all the dark and difficult years should now be turning their backs on him. I do not think there is any doubt that Timbo was being penalized for the energetic activities of his mother since, although I was in those days a potential source of much-needed funds, I was undoubtedly also a force to be reckoned with and my invitation to the media to join me in my campaign was looked upon with disapproval by the medical powers that be. Help came in the form of his charismatic transplant surgeon, Mick Bewick, whose wife Sue was a consultant at the renal unit at Dulwich Hospital. As soon as Timbo was strong enough to leave Guy's he began a long stint of night dialysis at Dulwich, enabling him, in theory, to continue his working life.

Travelling up to Waterloo Station on my daily hospital visits I had noted the commercial exhibitions which were often staged there. I decided that Waterloo Station would be an ideal setting for an exhibition with the theme 'Think about Kidney Donation' and I set about making suitable arrangements. Once again money was the problem. I have always felt a very acute responsibility to the donors to charitable funds and I do not believe that such funds should be spent on the hiring of halls or ballrooms for meetings or dances, or on stands or space for exhibitions or publicity, but would always rather give the opportunity for such facilities to be offered free of charge. My exhibition at Waterloo Station that year was staged in a display caravan loaned by Hoechst Pharmaceuticals, standing on space paid for by the DHSS and manned by myself and a series of volunteer nurses and doctors. If I had known then what I know now I would have found a better way of spending a week, but I genuinely

believed that with persistent publicity and increased availability the day would come when all caring British people
would carry the donor card.

More than ten years after the exhibition 'Think about
Kidney Donation' a Gallup survey showed that whilst 74 per
cent of the adult population were willing for their kidneys to
be used in transplant operations after the death, only 14 per
cent of those people actually carried a donor card. The kidney
donor card played an important part in creating awareness of
the need for kidney donation, and was used as a constant
reminder that people were dying because no cadaver kidneys
were being made available to save their lives. So why did so
few people carry one?

During the years I sought every opportunity to discuss the
problem on the radio and television and wrote endless articles
in national magazines. The reasons given by the general
public as to why they were not card-carriers were always the
same. The lack of availability of the cards themselves was one
very genuine reason. The feeling that carrying a donor card in
a wallet or handbag was giving daily acknowledgement to the
possibility of demise was another. There was also a strong
aversion on the part of the spouse or partner to write their
name in the space allowed for the signature of the next of kin
and it was wrongly believed that the permission of the next of
kin was still a legal requirement when signing the donor card.
Whilst the majority of the people in the country were
prepared for their kidneys to be used for transplant purposes
after their death, they were not on the whole disposed or
sufficiently motivated to go to the trouble of finding a kidney
donor card and remembering to carry it with them at all
times. I found apathy difficult to overcome, but to anyone
who was genuinely averse to kidney donation my advice was
always the same: 'If you cannot see yourself as a potential
kidney donor then think of yourself or your loved one as a
potential recipient and all your objections will melt away.'

By the beginning of that year I had become increasingly
aware of the needs of dialysis patients and their families, the

lack of facilities for patients requiring dialysis and transplantation, and the serious shortage of cadaver kidneys. The
National kidney Research Fund (NKRF) continued to
support the various renal research programmes being
undertaken up and down the country but there was no
association dedicated to the benefit and welfare of Britain's
kidney patients. My good friend, Lord Platt, a past President
of the Royal College of Physicians and a renal physician of
renown, was at that time one of the two sponsors of the
NKRF. We used to meet frequently and talk about the
inadequacies and attitudes of those responsible for the care of
renal patients and he was, I know, not entirely surprised when
I told him of my plans to form an association for kidney
patients and asked him to join me. We had just left a meeting
of the NKRF Committee where discussion had taken place
regarding the fact that the Director of Public Prosecutions
had been alerted to some irregularity in fund raising for the
Fund, which had come to light at a recent court case
concerning the illegal activities of a particular individual who
was also, in his spare time, fund raising at enormous profit to
himself. Without much difficulty I persuaded Robert Platt
that he could ill-afford to be associated with an organization
whose fund raising policies were under scrutiny by the
Charity Commissioners and he accepted my invitation to
lunch for immediate discussions concerning the founding of
the British Kidney Patient Association.

Robert Platt was a man of great integrity and understanding, with the milk of human kindness coursing through
his veins. He was, at that time, well into his seventies with a
lifetime of service behind him, which had been justly
recognized by both governments and his professional
colleagues. He was of the old school, and did not rely on
modern technology for diagnosis, but on his own clinical
judgement and he always said, 'If in doubt, ask the patient!' I
knew that if Robert Platt were to give me his support it
should not prove too difficult to attract a handful of well-
established, highly-thought-of renal physicians prepared to

form a Council of Management. Over a carafe of house wine in a modest Italian restaurant a seed was sown that day which later grew into the BKPA.

In July of that year, Nigel had given me an ultimatum. 'Either put your charitable work on a professional footing or stop it altogether. I will give you until the end of December.' Poor man, the bills had been getting heavier and heavier. Not only was he paying the salary of my secretary, covering all the cost of telephone calls, stationery, and stamps, but he was also picking up my travel expenses – which were enormous. In my anxiety to acquaint myself fully with the problems and needs of the patients, I was travelling many miles all over the country talking, where possible, to renal physicians, and visiting renal units both here and abroad. I knew that it would be unfair to look to Nigel for continued help so I approached Hoechst Pharmaceuticals, whose Managing Director had already shown interest in my work, and asked for their help with BKPA. All I needed, I told him, was a small grant for the first year to set me on my feet and give me an opportunity of raising funds in the earnest hope that my expenses would be covered.

My aim was to form an Association dedicated to the benefit and welfare of all kidney patients throughout the country, which would not only be able to take care of their financial and material needs and offer them support and advice, but also lobby the government for more facilities so that all patients requiring treatment could receive it. At the same time, it would create, through the media, awareness of the need for kidney donors and all the problems resulting from the lack of them.

Whilst details of Timbo's first transplant have been lost to me, I remember the second as if it were yesterday. It was a beautiful summer's evening and the date was Saturday 29 June 1974. We had returned from a cocktail party held in the lovely gardens of local friends, gone to bed early and had been asleep some hours when the telephone rang. Mick Bewick's voice came on the line: 'Can you get the boy up here quickly? We have a kidney for him!' With my heart pounding so that I could scarcely breathe, I said, 'But Mick, he's terribly unwell and frightfully anaemic. Is it going to be alright, is it safe?'

'Don't ask stupid questions!' was the reply. 'Get dressed all three of you and come up to Guy's as fast as you can.'

We were scared and unsure and 3 o'clock in the morning is no time for optimism. Timbo, I think, felt too ill to care very much, but he did remark from the back seat of the car on the drive up to London 'I wonder if it is safe to transplant me when I am so anaemic? I hope Mick doesn't lose too much blood.'

Within minutes of our arrival at Guy's he was in his white operating gown and lying on a trolley, and by half past four in the morning Timbo was in the theatre undergoing his second transplant operation and Nigel and I were waiting together in Sister's little sitting-room. We were sitting silently, both occupied with our own thoughts, fears and prayers, when suddenly Nigel looked across at me and said, 'I have just realized I have not got my kidney donor card with me. Have you got yours?'

'Of course not,' I replied. 'It's in my wallet at home; I've brought nothing with me, not even my handbag.'

I smiled to myself at the thought that there was I, a kidney donor card campaigner of the first degree, and yet on the mercy dash to London travelling at speeds exceeding 100 mph, breaking every rule in the Highway Code in our anxiety to get to the hospital in the shortest possible time, I had left my kidney donor card at home! The wait for news from the theatre seemed interminable, but at last, at 7 o'clock in the morning, Sister's door finally opened and a white-faced Mick Bewick stood in the doorway.

'Is everything alright?' I asked anxiously.

'Yes, fine,' he replied. Yet one look at his face was enough to tell me that, as I found out later, he had nearly lost Timbo on the operating table.

That summer found me back in London again after the

failure of Timbo's second transplant as his health was so precarious that it had become dangerous to have him with us in the country. So whilst everyone was commuting into London in the morning Nigel and I were driving out of London from our rented house to our offices in the country. Three mornings a week we dropped Timbo off at Dulwich Hospital for dialysis and returned to pick him up in the early evening, when he would go straight to bed. Although he was too weak to walk and had to be pushed in a wheelchair from the unit to the waiting car, he always insisted, on arriving at the house, on making his own way to his bedroom, climbing the stairs slowly but surely on all fours. His second transplant had been an utter disaster and we very nearly lost him. His transplant surgeon who, if he had a failing at all, erred on the compassionate side and was a good example of the heart ruling the head, found a kidney for Timbo in an endeavour to prevent him having to face life on dialysis once more. He was unprepared, both physically and emotionally, for the operation, was dangerously anaemic, and had not fully recovered from the traumas of the loss of his first graft. Two months after the second transplant operation, during which time he had never been off dialysis, they removed the kidney but the experiment had taken its toll.

Our time at Gladstone Street was probably one of the most unhappy in my life. It was weeks before Timbo got out of his pyjamas, which to me had become a symbol of sickness and defeat. On non-dialysis days I would stay up in London with him whilst Nigel made the trek back to the country and his office. My secretary opened my mail down there and we had a daily session on the telephone when she took dictation, arranged appointments, and gave me the names and telephone numbers of people who had rung in wishing to speak to me. With Nigel returning each evening bringing my letters for signature, I was somehow able to keep up the momentum of my work. Timbo would appear in the sitting-room, usually about midday, still in his pyjamas, letting me know that he was not yet ready to be pushed back into the living world. His friends, who were numerous, were constantly ringing with messages showing concern and affection or enquiring as to whether or not they would be welcome to visit him. He was, for the first time in his long years of illness, temporarily defeated and utterly shattered physically, mentally, and emotionally. He needed time to sort himself out, and regain his strength and purpose, and whilst I knew this and understood, I felt depressed and wretched.

As was always the case when Timbo himself was down and suffering he hit back at me, thus increasing my own unhappiness. Our early Victorian rented house in Gladstone Street was typical of many town houses built in that time with four floors and a basement kitchen. Nigel would spend his evenings on his return from the country watching the television with Timbo in his bedroom whilst I, knowing that I was unwelcome, spent my time in the basement kitchen. Banished below stairs with only the pavement grating to throw light on to my gloomy world, I longed for the peace and security of my country home. An artificial air of gaiety, produced by false laughter when taking the opportunity, whilst living temporarily in London, to entertain our many London-based friends, only served to enhance the feeling of unreality.

I was sitting in the kitchen one day reading the paper when Timbo appeared in the doorway fully dressed, and with a friendly smile and a 'Morning, what's for breakfast today?' he sat down at the kitchen table. Like the small, toy celluloid clown that he had had when he was a small boy, the shot had finally settled and he was upright once more. Then began the difficult and often tragic period when he was not strong enough to take part in young fun or well enough to feel willing to commit himself in advance, but his spirit was ready to take up the reins once more and join his friends in their fit and healthy worlds. I remember all too clearly one evening when I was quietly reading a book in the drawing-room at Gladstone Street and he was on the telephone trying to arrange a date for that evening. He was wearing a suit for the first time in many weeks, having smartened himself up especially for an occasion.

'Hi, David, I thought we might go to the pictures tonight, are you free?... Oh well, never mind. Perhaps another time... No, I'm afraid I can't next Friday, I'm dialysing.'

He tried four more friends, his spirits falling. Each time he dialled another number I prayed that that friend would be free. It was the same old story all over again and we had lived through it in his early days of dialysing when he was only seventeen or eighteen years old. When he felt well he was raring to go but he dare not commit himself to dates ahead because he knew from experience that what he felt like doing today he might not necessarily feel strong enough to do tomorrow. In fact, the first move he made outside the house was in a wheelchair with a friend who had agreed to wheel him round the Motor Show.

We stayed in London until I felt he was well enough to leave and two of his closest friends, who both happened to be flat hunting, moved in to live with him. He had by that time settled back into the old routine of night dialysis at Dulwich so one late Friday afternoon we packed the car and drove back to the country. When I said goodbye he seemed depressed and quiet but assured me he was only tired and had planned an early night. Upon my return to Oakhanger I rang his sister Becky, who was always willing and ready to check him out for me, and asked her to call in that evening and cheer him up. She rang me two hours later with the astounding news that she had been over to Gladstone Street but Timbo was nowhere to be found, the house was empty. I rang the hospital feeling sure that some disaster had occurred after my departure and that he had been re-admitted; they had no news of him. I rang his number from time to time throughout that week-end in the hope of finding him in, and was finally persuaded that as he was not in hospital all must be well and he had unexpectedly gone to stay with friends.

It was not in fact until Monday morning, when the hospital rang to say that he had been admitted, that I learned the true story. After we had left that Friday he decided on the spur of the moment to beat the blues and drive to Edinburgh on the off chance of securing tickets for the Rugby International at Murrayfield the next day. He persuaded one of his friends to accompany him and left around 7 o'clock that evening, driving himself through the night and arriving in Edinburgh at 5 o'clock the following morning. They found a hotel, had a bath, two hours sleep, and a large breakfast, and went to the ground, where they queued for four hours for tickets for the terraces. He then stood throughout the match in the bitter cold, drinking neat whisky from a hip-flask to keep warm, threw himself into bed that night, and drove the entire way back the following day arriving on time at the hospital for his Sunday night dialysis! Needless to say he was in no fit state to discharge himself and remained in hospital all that week recovering from his enterprising adventure, which he assured me was well worth the disapproval of the unit staff! Before I left Gladstone Street and returned to the country two of the directors of Hoechst Pharmaceuticals came to see me one afternoon to discuss the proposals that I had made in writing to their Managing Director.

'How much money do you think you would need for the first year?' they asked.

I was quite unprepared for the question. The first figure which came into my head as being more than enough to cover my ample needs was £1,200, but I rejected it and heard myself saying, 'Two thousand pounds will give me a start and hopefully in six months' time I could manage on my own.'

After they had left I cursed myself for being greedy and for getting over-excited and enthusiastic and waited anxiously for a letter confirming my own assessment of the meeting we had had. I could see the words written clearly on the headed notepaper: 'We have given careful consideration to your request but regret...' and the words threatened to take precedence over my preoccupation with Timbo's illness.

A letter arrived one week later letting me know that the Managing Director of Hoechst Pharmaceuticals was delighted to be able to support my venture and wished me luck!

At last I had the financial support that I needed, and with the most senior renal physician in the land as sponsor I set about gathering together an eminent Council of renal physicians and getting the approval of the Charity Commissioners. But these things cannot be done overnight and in the meantime, with Timbo's needs to see to as well as the needs of others, I settled down to caring for him and helping him back to health, knowing that what was now my dream would in time become reality. Patience has never been one of my attributes, however, and it was to be a frustrating year of set-backs and broken promises on the public side of my life, and much bitter disappointment on the private side, before the British Kidney Patient Association came into being on 29 September 1975.

By that time Timbo was faced with the prospect of 'no more transplants for at least another year', the breakup of his first real romantic relationship, the loss of his much-loved job at Sotheby's, and a future limited and frustrated by the need for dialysis. All of which, at twenty-one, took great courage to come to terms with and endure.

People do not live in order to dialyse, they dialyse in order to live, and if there is no quality of life or no reason for it then death becomes preferable. Timbo was out of work for more than six months after his compulsory resignation from Sotheby's, and it was painful to see him grow more and more discouraged. In an interview on the 'Today' programme with James Wilkinson, medical and scientific correspondent for the BBC, he was asked to share his feelings with us all.

'What makes you want to keep going Timothy?' asked James.

He replied without hesitation, 'My friends and family. I have known patients in hospital with me who were nothing like so sick, who turned their faces to the wall and died in hospital because they had no reason to come out. I am surrounded by a family and friends who love me and care for me and who are worth living for, but without them there would be no point.'

Certainly at that time there seemed very little point to all of us and perhaps I could be forgiven for praying again, as I had so often in the past: 'Oh please, God, let him live properly or let him die, but don't play games with him like this.'

Our wonderful friends, the Bonhams, in the shape of their daughter Eve, came to our rescue and gave Timbo the job of forming and running the new catalogue department at their auction galleries in Montpelier Street. As his health improved and his strength increased he began life over again, albeit still on dialysis, and his twenty-third birthday saw him tearing around Brands Hatch in a Formula IV car watched by his proud and doting parents, who had easily succumbed to his incredible birthday wish!

# 5

# The Quality of Mercy

Throughout the long years of night dialysis for Timbo at Dulwich he established a pattern which was only broken by hospitalization. He dialysed on Sunday, Tuesday, and Friday nights so that he could continue with his working life. He would arrive at the unit at around 6 o'clock on Tuesday and Friday evenings after work, and he came off the machine sometimes as late as 2 o'clock in the morning. Every weekend he returned home when he had finished and no matter how rigorous and exhausting the dialysis had been he would somehow manage to get to his car where, once sitting down, he assured me he was capable of driving any distance. On Friday nights I would sleep lightly, waiting to hear the sound of his car coming up the drive, often as late as 4 o'clock in the morning. His dragging footsteps would turn right at the top of the stairs and I could settle down to sleep knowing that he was safely home again with another week behind him. He would arrive home dead tired after a week in the office but all too often the blessed oblivion of sleep would be denied him because of cramp. He would fall into bed and almost immediately his feet and calves would be seized by excruciating pain only relieved by pressing his feet on the floor or walking around his bedroom. He confided in me once that he had difficulty in keeping from crying as he was so exhausted, and on these occasions would slip down to the kitchen and make himself a strong cup of hot Bovril in an often vain attempt to replace the salt which had been dialysed out of him.

His week-ends were given over entirely to recharging his batteries for the week ahead. He spent most of the time in front of the television set covered by a large fur car rug for warmth and comfort, in winter seldom moving from his chair in the morning-room, except for meals, and in the summer only venturing outside to sit by the swimming-pool. Occasionally he saw his friends on a Saturday, but on Sunday he refused all invitations for lunch since the threat of dialysis hung over him in the evening and he was, I think, afraid of becoming involved and having to tear himself away to drive to hospital before the party was over.

Because he was, in a way, an old campaigner – having endured and survived more than twenty operations including two failed transplants – he was in a position to bring comfort and reassurance to some of the newer patients having to face what he had already been through himself. He never told me of his mercy trips to Dulwich when he would leave home early after lunch on Sunday, although not needed in the hospital until that evening, but I heard from the Sister on the renal ward that often he would arrive earlier than necessary and visit a particular patient who was in trouble and anxious, in the hope of being able to set his mind at rest. From what some of the patients have said and written to me, I think he was a great source of comfort and strength to many of them. Just seeing him alive, smiling and chatting beside their beds, knowing what he had suffered and survived, must have given them the hope they so badly needed at that time. He was, I know, a tremendous champion of the underdog and on many occasions earned the displeasure and disapproval of the nursing staff, and even of doctors, by supporting those whom he felt less fortunate than himself. Equally he had no time or sympathy for those whom he termed 'the gutless or complaining', and he was scathing and derisive towards some of the unfortunate foreigners on the ward who had not been blessed with the inheritance of British grit and backbone.

All the night patients at Dulwich were expected to fill in their own charts, recording their temperature, blood pressure, and weight at intervals throughout their nightly dialysis. Timbo used his chart for leaving irate messages for the day staff, pointing out perhaps that the television sets were not working properly or that their supper had been cold when it was supposed to be hot, or for recording some of his thoughts and feelings at the time!

Over the years I have received many letters from patients and their loved ones expressing their appreciation of the kindness they have received at the hands of doctors and nursing staff. Sadly I have also received hundreds of letters from patients and their families complaining about their treatment or lack of it, voicing their protest at their doctors, and seeking my advice. Whilst I have always appreciated the need for tact and diplomacy and am careful to avoid disrupting the relationship between doctor and patient, I have never hesitated to take up cudgels on behalf of these people and attempt to sort out each individual problem.

One such opportunity occurred when the mother of a seven-year-old patient called Tina rang me one evening in floods of tears and explained that she had been told by the renal physicians at her local renal unit that little girls of seven were not put on kidney machines and that, with luck, Tina might have six months to live. Her mother was distraught with grief and begged me to save her daughter's life. I promised her that I would do what I could to help and immediately rang the renal consultant who had turned Tina away from treatment. The reason for denying Tina dialysis treatment when she needed it was simply staggering, and it took me some time to appreciate the significance of his words.

'My dear Mrs Ward, you have no idea of the background of this little girl or the type of family that she comes from. Her mother is inadequate and her father is an alcoholic.'

'Do you mean to tell me,' I replied, 'that this little girl is going to be sentenced to death because her mother is inadequate and her father drinks too much? There are thousands of children in this country in care who come from inadequate homes but they are not murdered.'

I asked the consultant after further conversation if he would be prepared for me to contact a paediatric nephrologist worthy of the description with a view to arranging for Tina to be treated when treatment was required, and he replied briskly, 'Go ahead, do as you please.'

I was fortunate enough to be able to contact the doctor that same night and he could promise me no more than that he would agree to see Tina and her mother and make his decision after the consultation. It is not hard to imagine the relief felt and expressed by Tina's mother when she received my late night call letting her know that I had been able to make an appointment for her daughter to be seen by one of the leading paediatric nephrologists in the country. Tina was taken onto the programme and for a full year she dialysed in the hospital, staying there from Monday to Friday like a weekly boarder, doing her lessons and receiving her treatment and returning to her 'inadequate home' each weekend. After eleven months on dialysis she received a kidney from her mother and picked up the pieces of her shattered childhood and is now a lovely fifteen year old with a full and happy life stretching before her.

Of course, I can't always publicize the stories I hear through private correspondence but I have taken good care of the press over the years and they have, in return, taken good care of me. I have always avoided the reporters writing for the sensational press and made friends instead with the medical reporters of the various established national newspapers, many of whom have taken the trouble to ring me and read over their report or story to check for inaccuracies. Other than divulging home telephone numbers of doctors and transplant surgeons, or putting them in direct touch with the patients and their relatives, I have always made it my business to be in a position to feed them with the information they require or to furnish them with the names of those best able to illustrate their stories. After all, they have a job of work to do as well, and time is of the essence with all journalists and reporters and if they can reduce the time spent in research by getting as many facts and figures as possible from one source, they are more likely to return to that source again. My time is also precious, but that spent in taking trouble with the press has been repaid a thousandfold.

After Timbo's first transplant a letter had been written and signed by myself and appeared on the front page of the *Sunday Express* on Christmas Eve. 'To the widow whom I shall never meet' was the headline. The letter read:

> Somewhere around this Christmas is a girl of 24 spending, perhaps, her first Christmas alone. A young widow whom I have never met, nor ever will, but who means so much to all of us.
>
> On March 21 this year, she lost her husband in a road accident and his tragic death meant life to my 19-year-old son, Timothy.
>
> Within minutes of her husband's death, when asked, she offered his kidneys to Timothy's surgeon. I would like to think that she might know what this meant to him... to all of us – and may draw a little comfort from knowing...

The precedent created by my letter was that the signature was my own and not that of Max Aitken! My first press conference, held in the old press club in Fleet Street, attracted an amazing amount of interest. The subject was the introduction of the donor card and whilst I was nervous in the extreme, I was immensely gratified to observe the attention that I received. My old friend Mick Bewick, the transplanter from Guy's, was with me and when his turn came to answer questions his enthusiasm led to an indiscretion. Jumping to my feet, I told the assembled company, 'I want you all to put a thick, black line through that last remark,' and sat down again. Afterwards I was approached by John Stevenson, a reporter from the *Daily Mirror*, who had been a great supporter of mine and had given me much needed help and advice.

'Young woman, let me give you a word of warning. You do not tell the press ever what they may write and what they may not write or you will get yourself into real deep trouble.'

I took his words to heart and since then have never 'told', only asked!

Unfortunately a good attendance for one press conference does not necessarily mean a good attendance for the next. I have on many occasions been bitterly disappointed at the press turnout for something which I had myself felt to be of national importance, and on many others utterly amazed at the genuine interest shown in a quite unimportant event, such as the day I took a handful of young kidney patients to see round the Tower of London and have tea with the Governor. Fifteen children on dialysis and six who had been transplanted, all of school age, found themselves surrounded by eager, questioning reporters and cameramen jostling for the best position. This child was posed with that one, and then another, in front of the car, with the ravens, or on the drawbridge; this story was taken, and then that one, whilst the children clamoured excitedly to attract the attention of the keenest reporter. They certainly ended that outing in no doubt of their importance, but the following morning saw not one column-inch reported in any paper, either national or otherwise, and bitter disillusionment was the order of the day. On the other hand, at something as important as the inaugural meeting of the founding of the Association only two members of the press turned up, one being a freelance journalist hoping to get a story in a woman's magazine, and the other an elderly hack, reputed to be writing for the local newspaper, whose only obvious interest in the proceedings was the free drink at the end. Sadly that got no coverage either.

On my grant of £2,000 from Hoechst Pharmaceuticals, which

I was given in September 1974, I raised £64,000 over the next twelve months so that by the time I was ready to launch the new Association in September 1975 I was able to cope with the increased expenses, as well as being in a position to give a considerable donation to Guy's Hospital. I was fortunate in that my husband worked from home and we already had two offices, one in which we worked ourselves and the other given over to our two secretaries and a telex machine. It was, therefore, both unnecessary and inappropriate – because of Timbo's constant need for me – that I should look elsewhere to headquarter the BKPA. Quite apart from the convenience to myself, the saving on administrative costs was considerable as both offices could be occupied by myself and my secretary free of all charge, as is still the case today.

With regard to the formation of my Council I was anxious not only to have serving men of calibre, and giants in their field, but also I felt it essential that they should be representative of the different areas of medicine involved with renal dialysis and transplantation. My first Council comprised one paediatrician, one biochemist, two transplanters, and two renal physicians. Bishop Huddleston joined Robert Platt as a sponsor and I became the self-elected President. There are many ethical issues involved in the medical care of the sick, and perhaps nowhere more so than with renal patients, and I wanted those issues to be taken into account. I knew Trevor Huddleston to be a churchman not only of standing, but of great courage, and I was very anxious to have his support and involvement. I wrote to him, as a complete stranger out of the blue, and received in reply a letter inviting me to take lunch with him at his house in Stepney, where he was Bishop. He is a man of such obvious devotion not only to duty, but – more importantly – to people from all walks of life, race, and creed, and, of course, colour. I came away from lunch that day both proud and pleased that he had accepted my invitation to act as sponsor to the Association, and knowing that I had the backing of someone who would never flinch from saying publicly what he felt to be right, no matter how unpopular his stand might be. He has been a source of enormous strength to me over the years, both spiritually and otherwise, and I have grown to love him dearly.

Normally the setting up of a charity is an expensive business since the whole package must be presented by lawyers to the Charity Commissioners for their ruling and acceptance. I am fortunate enough to have one of the best lawyers in the country who, apart from charging me for the company seal – which he did with much apology – has never made a charge for anything at all since the charity was founded. It is true that he is an old friend, which is, of course, why I chose him in the first place, and certainly I am the godmother of his eldest son, but since my charity's need for legal advice and action has continued to increase to alarming proportions over the years. I would like to acknowledge the enormous debt that I owe to Clifford Chance – and to Simon Burgess in particular. From complicated wills and the conveyancing of overseas properties for holiday dialysis centres, to restructuring the Articles of Association and guiding us through the legal requirements of our biannual meetings, the practical help given to me by this firm of expert solicitors must be worth thousands of pounds each year and my gratitude is boundless.

In February 1976 Timbo was once more fighting for his life in Dulwich Hospital. He had so often over the years been admitted to hospital for some quite minor reason, only to present with some fearful unimagined complication, and this was just such an occasion. Steroids from past treatment had been responsible for benign tumours appearing in various parts of his body, which necessitated surgery once more. I had made two appointments in Birmingham before his admission, one for lunch with Dick White, the paediatric nephrologist at the Children's Hospital in Ladywood, and one later that afternoon to visit a large comprehensive school of some 1,500 children and to receive an even larger cheque from the headboy. I drove to London early, calling at

Dulwich Hospital on my way to the station to have a few
words with Timbo, but on arrival I found the screens were up
around his bed. I had expected to find him cheerfully
recovering from minor surgery and had planned to tell him
that on my way back from Birmingham I would call in and
spend an hour with him. It seemed, however, that during the
night he had been overwhelmed by agonizing pain in no way
connected with the operation of the day before. I spoke with
the doctor, who emerged reluctantly from behind the screens,
and he told me that he was very concerned about Timbo but
until he had had the results of the tests he planned to make he
was not able to set my mind at rest. If I was to keep my
appointment and catch the train I had to leave immediately,
yet, understandably, my heart urged me to remain. I was glad
later that I did not succumb to the dictates of my heart that
day, since the outcome of my visit to Birmingham proved to
be of outstanding importance.

It had been the policy of most, if not all, renal physicians to
disguise the truth when being forced to sentence their patients
to death. Facilities for patients requiring dialysis treatment
were limited then, as indeed they are today, and as a result of
those limitations patient-selection was being carried out. In
Birmingham there were no dialysis facilities for children at
all, and very few children from the Birmingham area received
dialysis treatment when their kidneys failed. They were
offered the alternative, which was death. Dick White told me
over lunch that day that a number of his young patients,
twenty-four was the number he gave, I remember, had died
over the past five years simply because he had no dialysis
facilities to offer them. The few children who had been
accepted reluctantly by the adult dialysis unit at the East
Birmingham Hospital fared very badly and, in his opinion,
two of them had died for no other reason than that the staff
and medical team looking after them were not, quite
naturally, conversant with the problems of paediatric
patients. Treatment and care of children on dialysis is not the

same as that for adults, though many adult nephrologists would claim it is.

I was horrified to hear that the parents of these children were not told the truth, but were made to believe that even if dialysis facilities were available their child could not benefit for medical reasons. The truth of the matter, of course, was that their child *would* have benefited since its life could have been saved, but without the facilities death was inevitable. Dick argued that the parents already had enough to cope with in the knowledge of the impending death of their beloved child without the added burden of knowing that their child's death was unnecessary. I argued that it was preposterous that these parents, who had every right to know the truth, should be denied it, being at the same time denied the possibility of seeking help elsewhere and of voicing their protest to the Government. My argument was so strong as to convince Dick, and from that day until the time when dialysis facilities for children became available in Birmingham I believe he told the parents the truth.

I arrived at the school in a sombre mood and sitting on the dais beside the headmaster, looking down on the upturned faces of over 1,000 healthy children, I thought, 'You have raised all this money for kidney patients and yet if any of you should ever need treatment on a kidney machine you will not receive it.'

I was determined to make this fact public knowledge and turned to friends in the media. Both radio and television have played an important part in the fortunes of the BKPA and have done much to bridge the gap between those who have and those in need, so on my return that evening I rang James Wilkinson and told him of my concern. Fortunately he shared it and did a piece with me there and then over the telephone to be recorded the following morning on the 'Today' programme.

I was in my office at 8.50 a.m. when the phone rang and a voice asking for me said: 'It is Cliff Smith here. I am the

Chairman of the Birmingham Lions and I have just heard you on my car radio driving to the office. Is it true that children are dying in the Birmingham area because there are no kidney machines for them?'

I told him that it was indeed the truth and that unless money could be raised to build a small, paediatric unit there would surely be more small crosses erected in local graveyards.

'Don't worry,' he assured me, 'I will do something about this, I promise,' and hung up.

The Birmingham Lions raised £78,000 in less than forty weeks and a purpose-built dialysis unit specially for the children was attached to the side of the East Birmingham Hospital. A young kidney patient not yet requiring dialysis treatment joined Cliff Smith and me at a ceremony for the laying of the foundation stone; but by the time the unit was built Philip Long had died. The facilities had come too late to save him.

Timbo recovered from his recent ordeal, and was out of hospital two weeks later, but it was not the only time the BKPA came before the needs of my family. Another occasion that I remember was on the birth day of my only grandson, Charles. Susie had come to stay with me for two weeks before the date marked for the baby's arrival. I had kept the four days prior to that date free from all appointments so that I could drive her to the hospital and hold her hand. The week before the baby was expected I was working on some papers when a pinched, strained face appeared round the office door.

'Mummy, I think the baby is coming. What do I do?'

My immediate reaction was one of horror. 'It can't be, I have an appointment in London for lunch today and I can't possibly break it!'

Poor Susie, she must have been as horrified as I at such an unexpected reaction and the apparent rejection of her need by her loving mother. I had, in fact, arranged to meet the mother of a young kidney patient whom I had been supporting for some time and who was anxious to form a fund-raising branch of the BKPA. I had invited her and two other relatives of kidney patients to lunch that day and there was no way that I could contact them to cancel our meeting. Much as I would have preferred to have driven Susie to hospital and to have been around to support her during the birth of her baby, I felt that my commitment to Vivian and her friends must be honoured, and I could only hope that Susie would understand. The Bromley branch of the BKPA was formed that day as we sat at the lunch table drinking in white wine the health of our new baby.

I have never had a specific policy to form fund-raising branches of the BKPA – they have simply evolved. The majority of our thirty-two branches today cover the country, albeit inadequately, reaching as far north as Inverness and south-west to Plymouth. They are run either by the patients themselves or by close relatives and many have written to me since forming a branch expressing their delight and surprise on finding that they were, unbeknown to them, surrounded by so many people who really cared. But I see their activities as a form of much-needed therapy rather than as a reliable contribution to the fund because it is sad, but understandable, that people on the whole like to support their own local cause and in a sense, therefore, the BKPA branches are in direct competition with the local fund raising that is being carried out in support of the local renal unit.

Patients and relatives have often launched themselves enthusiastically into fund raising to show their appreciation of the practical support they have received from the Association, and have written telling me – with pride – that they have, through some event or other, been able to raise a large sum of money – which they have then presented to the consultant at their renal unit! One patient, whose university fees and accommodation we were paying for during his three-year course, drove all the way down from the Midlands in his tiny car to tell me how delighted he knew I would be to learn that he had raised over £600 as a result of a sponsored run.

'That's absolutely marvellous, John, thank you so much. Have you got the cheque with you now?' I asked.

'Oh no,' was his reply. 'I gave that to my consultant when I was at clinic the other day.'

Bless their hearts, I often wonder where they think we get our own funds from – without which, as they have so often told me, they would be lost.

By the end of that first year, in addition to energetic fund raising, I began to seek every possible avenue which would lead to publicity concerning the shortage of facilities for patients with end-stage renal failure in the country. Understanding by this time the type of story likely to attract press interest, I had to produce a great number of different variations on a theme. I began spreading my net in an attempt to attract publicity. 'Over-Prescribing Denies Aid To Kidney Patients' and 'Ennals Asks Patients To Cut Drug Demand' are good examples of the kidney story threatening to overshadow the *real* purpose of the articles, which was to draw attention to the vast sums of Health Service money being spent by GPs on unnecessary drug prescriptions. I made the most of every opportunity that was offered and have only once been known to make 'no comment' in response to press enquiries.

At the end of 1976 Timbo was once more up on his feet, willing and able to face another round, so we decided to spend Christmas abroad and went to Lermoos in Austria. We borrowed a portable dialysis machine from his renal unit and drove with it to Austria in a small car packed with the equipment and disposables, whilst Timbo and Becky flew out to meet us there. We chose the hotel with care, thinking that Timbo would have neither the strength nor the inclination to spend much time on the slopes but that, hopefully, he would find compensation in the heated swimming-pool and sauna. I wanted so much for this Christmas to be a special one to make up for those gone before when he had driven down from London after dialysis on Christmas Eve, spent an exhausting Christmas Day with us, and driven back again on Boxing day to dialyse once more that night.

On arrival at the beautiful snow-clad resort of Lermoos we realized at once how wise we were to have chosen a hotel with so many amenities. The lower, and nearest, ski slopes lay a good uphill mile from our hotel and the only practical way to reach them was on foot. I could not imagine that Timbo, in his state of health, would possibly cope with the athletic programme expected of him, but not for the first time I had underestimated his amazing strength and will-power. He walked with the rest of us each morning with his skis over his shoulders in his stiff unyielding ski boots, and having spent all morning on skis collapsed exhausted after lunch whilst we returned to the slopes without him. There are some good memories of that Christmas; however, I think it one best forgotten. The cold, stark fact staring us all in the face was that Timbo was really sick and, no matter how much he wanted it otherwise, the doors of sport had closed on him for ever. I found it near impossible to enjoy myself and, more importantly, to give pleasure to the others if Timbo was unable to share in activities with us.

By the end of 1977, a year later, Timbo had had a reasonably uninterrupted year at Bonham's with only four admissions to hospital; the BKPA fund was standing at well over £200,000, the number of column-inches covering the shortage of dialysis facilities and cadaver donor kidneys was mounting, and I had begun to turn my attention towards the urgent need for holidays for dialysis patients and those who help them regularly with their treatment at home. In 1970 there had been a fearsome outbreak of serum hepatitis, spreading rapidly through many of the renal units in the country and in some causing the death of both medical and nursing staff. The reaction of the renal physicians was immediate and understandable. The exchange of patients between units for holiday dialysis was stopped, and it was no longer possible, for example, for a patient in Newcastle wishing to holiday on the south coast to visit either the Royal

Sussex Hospital at Brighton or St Mary's Hospital, Portsmouth, to receive treatment whilst he and his family were having a much-needed break.

Many of the units made no provision for holidays for their patients at all but a few of them, relenting to the pleas of their patients but lacking both time and imagination, had acquired holiday caravans and placed them in the grounds of some hospital near the sea. Their home patients, together with their long-suffering spouse or parent, could get a change of scene but little else. The renal physicians encouraged dependence upon the unit and discouraged any adventurous spirit anxious to integrate dialysis into a normal life – unless, of course, it was a working one! Most of the dialysis patients in those days seemed prepared to accept a situation where holidays, like so many other things, had become joys of the past, and they were encouraged to feel that their medical condition could not be managed away from the influence of their renal unit. Week after week, month after month, and all too often year after year, both the patient and his family were tied to the rigours of thrice-weekly dialysis, with no relief of any kind.

I had always fought the label 'disabled' for my own son, although I knew that such a label had advantages (indeed, when he discovered them himself he was not slow in making use of them), so that the idea of dialysis patients and their families mixing with fit and healthy holiday-makers in a normal holiday atmosphere had seemed to me an essential part of their rehabilitation. I was well aware that there were many renal physicians in the country who viewed my activities with a mixture of mistrust and scepticism and, therefore, thought it was important to be able to talk a track record before embarking on the holiday scheme that I had already set my heart on, so I started in a small way.

I thought it would be rather nice and special if I could persuade the Hampshire Scouts to accept half a dozen young male dialysis patients to become the next-best thing to 'King for a day', which was Scouts for a fortnight. I approached the

Commissioner of the Hampshire Scouts and explained to him the limitations, frustrations, and restrictions of life on dialysis and he gladly and enthusiastically agreed to give his support to an experimental venture whereby these boys, with portable dialysis machines set up in the warden's office, could join the Scouts at their permanent campsite in the New Forest. Three young patients from the Royal Free Hospital in London and three from Guy's were dialysed on the campsite by the units' nurses, who travelled by train to Hampshire, withdrawing discreetly when their treatment was over.

Not only was the experiment an unqualified success but it also opened my eyes to some of the problems that I had not foreseen. Reluctance, for example, on the part of several of the mothers to relinquish their sons to a normal holiday. Their anxiety was obvious and genuine and one unfortunate boy missed what seemed to him a golden opportunity because his mother refused to let him go unless she accompanied him and I drew the line at a son turning up at a Scout camp with his mother in tow.

Also interesting was the attitude of the Scout masters and the Scouts themselves, who freely admitted that when they heard that dialysis patients were going to join them for a week or two, had expected, as one boy put it, that they would be 'sick and weedy chaps not able to take part in all the things we did'. The young patients themselves, however, sportingly took part in rock climbing, canoeing, and building their own bivouacs, whilst two of them even managed a four-mile hike much to the amazement of both their mothers. They had obviously been treated previously as sick children, which indeed they were, but perhaps not enough thought had been given to their potential. One day, God willing, these boys would grow up to become men and a childhood devoid of childish things makes for an unbalanced manhood. Without the full support of their children's doctors and the devoted dedication of the nursing staff, they would never have had a chance to tell the story of 'when I was at Scout camp'.

In November, 1977, I received a letter giving me the astounding news that I was to be made a Member of the Order of the British Empire. I was unashamedly delighted not only with the honour bestowed upon me personally, but because I knew that a recognition of my work showed a recognition of the plight of kidney patients in our country. Nigel, not for the first time, tried to pull me sharply back to earth by reminding me sternly that I was an Englishwoman, not an Italian, and that my unbounded joy was both unseemly and unwarranted.

'I wonder if you will go to Buckingham Palace to collect it?' he remarked. 'I know that in the War MBEs were just sent through the post.'

I hoped, of course, that I would be invited to Buckingham Palace and that it would be my beloved Queen who would bestow on me my decoration, but I kept that hope to myself. On New Year's Eve when the Honours List was published I saw with disappointment that the words that I had longed to see after my name, 'For services to kidney patients', were missing, since without them there was no cause for my recognition.

Looking back on the outstanding events of that year, three other occasions I feel are worthy of mention. The first was in early spring when I had been invited by Harlech Television to appear on a magazine programme. Also appearing on the programme that afternoon was Joan Bakewell, the well-known columnist and TV presenter. On the long train journey back from Bristol to London we sat together and I had ample opportunity of acquainting her with the work of the Association and the problems arising out of lack of facilities for treatment and the shortage of cadaver kidneys for transplantation. On her return she immediately wrote a strongly emotive piece in her Sunday column, urging readers to become kidney donors and carry their cards. In April, when an opportunity presented itself on Granada Television's 'Reports Action' programme to appeal for trading stamps and cigarette coupons to swell the funds of the BKPA she eagerly took it. It was the first time that Granada Television had ever launched an appeal of that kind and they were quite unprepared, as indeed was I, for the staggering response.

Three thousand four hundred and twenty-nine mail-bags arrived at the Manchester headquarters of Granada Television over a period of three and a half weeks, but it took me over fourteen months to get them opened. By the end of the first week mail-bags were piled high against the walls of the canteen at Granada headquarters, whilst at the Securior depot across the way mail-bags were stacked from floor to ceiling in every available place, and the company's premises at Aldershot were likewise filled with bags from wall to wall. Whilst being utterly delighted at the response to the appeal I was genuinely horrified as the mail-bags continued to pour in, so that as a last resort I was forced to persuade the Garrison Commander at Bordon Camp to allow us to put the remainder in the cells!

The problem of opening the bags, sorting the contents, and despatching the trading stamps and cigarette coupons daily to the various addresses for redemption seemed, on the face of it, insurmountable. My staff at that time consisted of my secretary and an office junior, so without delay I personally set about the task of ensuring that the maximum amount of revenue be extracted in the shortest possible time from the result of a single ten-minute appeal on a national television network.

Fortunately, some four or five years previously my husband had built in the grounds of our home a guest-house which, being little used, I persuaded him to allow me to use as an Appeals Office and this little cottage now became the centre of the most amazing activity. I appealed locally, with the help of the local newspaper group, for volunteer sorters and over the months we welcomed Scouts, Guides, members of the WI, Rotary Club, and Round Table, off-duty soldiers from the nearby camps, and a small band of patients and relatives, some of whom are still sorting for us today. Even so, it was unreasonable to expect that the excitement and enthusiasm engendered by the response to the appeal would continue until the job was done and gradually the helpers faded away, leaving me with 1,600 mail-bags still unopened.

Other methods had to be tried and if Muhammad would not come to the mountain then we would take the mountain to Muhammad. I appealed again through the local press for volunteers prepared to open the mail-bags and sort the contents on site, and the response was gratifying. Saturdays and Sundays, lunchtimes and evenings, found us driving our precious cargo to factories, canteens, Methodist and Church Army halls, offices and stores; anywhere, in fact, where a number of workers were gathered together and could be persuaded to help. I commandeered the garrison cinema two evenings a week and volunteer soldiers, overseen by two kind and helpful sergeants, eagerly reported to participate in the local phenomenon.

Every morning a large Securicor van would arrive at the cottage filled with twenty or thirty mail-bags, and each evening at precisely 5.00 p.m. the van returned empty to be filled with sorted bags whose precious contents remained in safety overnight on Securicor premises until they could be despatched to their destinations for redemption the following day. It should go on record that during those early months the company charged us not one single penny for the storage of the mail-bags and the twice-daily runs. A contribution of such magnitude that it would have been hard for me to have found words at that time to have described my gratitude.

The utter selflessness of the viewers who had responded immediately, and with such overwhelming generosity, to the appeal was only matched some years later when the BKPA was fortunate enough to be chosen as the charity to benefit from a Blue Peter appeal. Neat bundles of cigarette coupons, which had been so carefully stored until the magic number had been reached when the collector could send in for a tea-set or a steam iron; shoe boxes and carrier-bags full of Green Shield or Co-op stamps, carefully hoarded against the day

when that longed-for summer holiday could be reached by
the redemption of hundreds of books; and smaller parcels,
addressed in a thin, spidery hand enclosing maybe half a
dozen books with a message telling us that the enclosed 'were
meant to buy a new teapot but your need is much greater than
mine'. Those were halcyon days indeed, when I was
surrounded by such loving warmth and blessed understanding that the sun shone brightly out of a dark and stormy sky
so that I felt its rays warming us all. By July of the following
year, the last mail-bag being opened, I knew that nearly half a
million pounds had been raised and according to the
*Guinness Book of Records* for that year it was the largest
amount ever raised in one single appeal in the history of
world television.

The second highlight of that year was the arrival of
Laurence Scragg, who joined me in June 1978, ostensibly to
take charge of fund raising. I had already realized that if the
BKPA were to expand and grow in the way that I wished,
then not only did I need additional accommodation for
expansion but I also needed personnel. I had been running
the charity entirely on my own for little short of three years
and executive help was much needed, although I was loath to
pay for it! I advertised the post of Appeals Organizer through
the Retired Officers' Association in the belief that I would
find a man of exceptional ability and sterling qualities,
steeped in loyalty, with a history of man-management and
dedication to duty, who, already being on a pension and
anxious to fill his twilight years with gratification, would be
willing to accept a very small salary in return! I received a
number of applications from an assortment of worthy ex-
serviceman and from a short list of four selected a retired
Army Major who has proved over the years to live up to all
my expectations. Starting as Appeals Organizer, promoted
to Appeals Director, switching to Finance Officer, and finally
to Administrator, he has become my right-hand man and
although we have recently taken on the services of a full-time
Finance Officer, Laurence and I today run the Association

together with six indispensable clerical staff.

The last event of significant importance that year affected us all personally. Timbo decided to bring home with him a portable dialysis machine at Christmas, which he borrowed from his renal unit, so he would not have to drive back to London on Boxing Day and would also be able to take full advantage of the extra day's holiday before Christmas. He dialysed with the family around him in the morning-room, his new dog beside him on the sofa, and whilst I had no opportunity of pretending for one moment that dialysis was no longer part of my life, his presence made it much easier to enjoy our holiday and, for that year, removed the guilt we always felt when he returned to his unit on Boxing Day leaving us behind to enjoy ourselves. It was very difficult for him, surrounded by his festive-spirited family, all eating and drinking with gay abandon, to adhere to his strict diet and his daily fluid allowance and it would be foolish to pretend that the holiday was unmarred by his illness, but we all felt much happier when we were, in a sense, able to share in the limitations and frustrations of his life. I prayed that next year he would be set free and the following Christmas would see us once more a happy family laughing and loving under a cloudless sky.

Timbo, aged eleven, with his dog, Zooloo

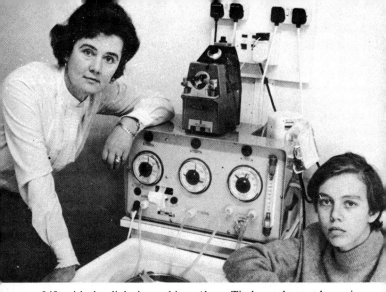

Life with the dialysis machine. *Above:* Timbo and me at home in 1972.
*Below:* Timbo enjoying a book while dialysing on our skiing holiday in Lermoos, Austria. This was Christmas 1976

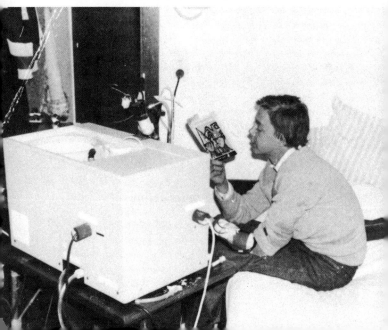

*Above:* The inaugural meeting of the BKPA in 1975 at the Institute of Directors, Belgrave Square, London. From left to right: Trevor Huddleston, Richard Bachelor (immunologist), Robert Sells (transplanter), Peter Morris (transplanter of Nigel's kidney to Timbo), Stewart Cameron (renal consultant), Martin Barratt (senior consultant of the renal clinic, Great Ormond Street), and Timbo *(Keystone Press)*

*Below:* Timbo, the dogs and me outside the house in the summer of 1975

Outside Buckingham Palace on 14 March 1978, after collecting the MBE, with Becky, Nigel and Timbo *(Press Association)*

The last mail-bag to be sorted from Manchester which arrived over a period of three and a half weeks as a result of Granada TV's 'Reports Action' programme. . . . Here I am with young kidney patients, including Tina Maslen (far right), the little girl whose life I saved. She is now a lovely seventeen year old, enjoying a happy life

*Below:* Timbo looking radiant in Australia. He had hoped to start a new life there

SACK NO
3429

*Above:* Nigel and Timbo, the weekend before the transplant operation in which they were both involved

*Right:* Timbo gives the thumbs up after receiving Nigel's kidney, September 1980

*Above:* The Duke of Edinburgh visits the holiday dialysis centre at Earnley, near Bracklesham Bay, West Sussex, July 1982

*Below:* One of my many carol concerts at St Peter's, Eaton Square, where I never had any difficulty attracting stars and media personalities. Seen here are Michael Aspel, Michael Redgrave and Lizzy Aspel in the front row, and Simon Ward in the second row *(Keystone Press)*

Timbo with Susy in May 1983, one month before they were married *(Woman's Own)*

# 6

# Holidays with a Difference

My prayers were answered to some extent, in that 1979 was a comparatively trouble-free year for Timbo, despite the thrice-weekly dialysis, but by the beginning of 1980 Timbo's health was beginning to deteriorate; he was constantly in trouble on the machine, and his life seemed to be slowly running to a stop. The decision had been taken some years previously to remove his own kidneys, which were the cause of persistent high blood pressure and all the related problems, but the price he had to pay for the control of his blood pressure was a low haemoglobin and the resulting persistent anaemia began to make life impossible for him. He had come to rely on regular blood transfusions for an adequate supply of iron, four units of blood every five to six weeks, but whilst normal, healthy kidneys can adequately cope with the day to day intake of iron, the dialysis machine cannot, and consequently deposits of iron were accumulating in his liver and his heart, threatening to grind those organs to a halt. His doctor was well aware of the possibility of having to face iron-storage problems, and I know he did his best to try and prolong the period between transfusions, but Timbo was adamant if he was going to be able to continue to work and get any pleasure out of life at all then these regular transfusions must continue and we seemed caught between the devil and the deep blue sea. I became immensely depressed over his condition and horrified at the prospect of

the slow destruction of his vital organs, so that the thought of
Timbo's future – or possible lack of it – filled my waking life
and was the cause of many sleepless nights.

Despite Timbo's deteriorating health he was determined to
get the last drop out of life, so although I was dismayed I was
not surprised when he asked me if I could arrange for him to
have dialysis in Melbourne! He wanted very much to go to
Australia for the Third Test Match that year, and stay with
his great friend, Clive Standish, who was at one time engaged
to Becky. Clive, a banker by profession, had since married an
Australian girl and he had settled in Melbourne with his
young wife Vicky. He was a charming person whom we had
known for some time as he was originally a friend of Timbo's
before succumbing to the charms of his sister! They had lived
together for a time in our rented house in Gladstone Street
and when we returned the house to its owner they moved on
to Battersea and lived together there.

Timbo's new transplant surgeon, Peter Morris, at the
Churchill Hospital, Oxford, was an Australian himself, and
with his help I was able to arrange dialysis for Timbo at
Prince Henry's Hospital in Melbourne for the six weeks of his
stay. He left on 21 January on what was an exciting adventure
for him and a true testing time for myself, since apart from a
two-week holiday in Ireland with friends and three weeks
spent in the South of France the summer before it was the
longest time by far that he had been apart from me since his
illness had forced him to leave Harrow at the age of
seventeen.

Although anxious in the extreme I was, of course,
delighted that he should have such a wonderful opportunity
to enjoy some independence and have a small slice of his life
that he could call his own. He told me once that he felt he had
lived in a goldfish bowl since he was thirteen years old and
longed for freedom and the opportunity of telling us what he
wanted us to know instead of feeling that we knew it all! His
visit went without mishap and whilst, of course, I longed to
know that all was well I contented myself with the thought

that any worrying situation would surely be immediately reported to me, and I convinced myself – with difficulty – that no news was good news. He was immensely happy throughout his stay and returned determined to go back to Australia and seek his fortune there when he was free of the machine once more. He made many friends and during the week-ends when they were free he went camping, white-water canoeing, horse-riding, and even managed to crack a small bone in his back playing cricket. I was as relieved and happy to have him back at the end of February as he must have been regretful at having to leave Clive and Vicky and all the young fun that he enjoyed in that beautiful country, despite the limitations forced on him by his failing health.

While he was away, Nigel and I were dining with our old friend Robert Sells, the Liverpool transplanter, one evening and for the first time we voiced our fears in public. Timbo had already been told that the chances of a third transplant were remote since, to quote his transplant surgeon, he had 'antibodies against the whole world'! Nigel put to Robert the possibility of Timbo receiving one of his kidneys in a live related donor operation, chancing that the knowledge acquired over the years might have exploded the theory that, since Timbo's renal disease was genetic, a kidney donated by either of us would be unacceptable. It had already been acknowledged some months previously that the expertise in the field of tissue typing being carried on at the Churchill Hospital, Oxford, was superior to that of any other renal unit in the country. Whilst his doctors at Dulwich felt that the chances of Timbo's ever being able to receive a third transplant were remote, at Oxford they had felt that there was at least a possibility. After a long and anxious discussion Robert Sells returned to Liverpool in no doubt as to the seriousness of Timbo's medical condition and the genuine desire of Nigel to donate one of his own kidneys to save Timbo's life. Peter Morris, the transplanter at the Churchill Hospital, was prepared to consider using one of Nigel's kidneys, so Nigel went through the normal thorough examination, both physical and emotional, given to all prospective live related donors. He passed all tests with flying colours and the date of the operation was fixed for 1 September that year.

I knew, of course, that there was a real possibility that things could go wrong and that we would lose Timbo, but in my heart of hearts I was sure that God would never allow him to return to the life that he had been leading as a young, frustrated, semi-invalid and, therefore, either the kidney would work and allow him freedom from his trials once more, and a return to normal living, or I could accept his death – to me the only alternative – as a merciful release from a life which sometimes seemed to him no longer worth having. I had met too many fit and healthy parents who had donated one of their kidneys to a child to have the smallest concern for Nigel's health, but naturally the thought of being separated from him to face alone the traumas of Timbo's transplant was too awful to be long considered, so with months to go before the operation I busied myself with the needs of the other patients.

One of the many matters that continued to concern me deeply was the lack of dialysis facilities for patients wishing to go on holiday. When dialysis becomes a necessity for life, like so many other things, holidays become joys of the past. The patient sits on the edge of his bed making up his machine for the umpteenth time and wonders where on earth he is going to find the strength and courage to face whatever the rest of the year might bring. Holidays I felt, therefore, for dialysis patients and, of course, for those that loved and cared for them, seemed to me to be one of their greatest needs. The demands made by the kidney machine on all members of the patient's family when he dialysed at home were stringent and relentless, and a break from the chore and responsibility for one or two weeks a year was essential if the family were to survive as a unit.

Some of the more enlightened consultants, still seriously

concerned by the possibility of another outbreak of serum hepatitis, had nevertheless conceded to the need for holidays and had eagerly accepted the offer of a caravan or chalet which, with their help and approval, could be equipped with dialysis facilities for one patient at a time. Usually these facilities were to be found in the grounds of a hospital by the sea, in complete isolation from all but the sick, or visiting relatives, not because the doctors thought that their patients would choose to continue with their hospital connections on vacation, but because alternative sites were hard to come by and the busy doctors gratefully accepted what was offered. I felt, myself, that what was needed was a holiday dialysis centre situated near the sea in the grounds of an existing holiday camp or village, where patients and their families would be surrounded by fit and healthy holiday-makers in a normal holiday atmosphere. I knew, of course, that my idea would be met either by polite rejection or genuine scepticism by many of the renal physicians, with whom I was nevertheless on friendly terms, so I decided that it would be better to present them with a *fait accompli* than to ask their opinion and advice!

I was fortunate enough to find myself at luncheon one day sitting beside Sir William Butlin, and I confided in him my idea of establishing a holiday dialysis centre in the grounds of a holiday camp. He was as enthusiastic as his great age would allow and suggested that I contact his son Bobby since he had, of course, by that time retired to Jersey, and he added: 'Tell him the old man thinks it is a good idea.'

I got in touch with Bobby Butlin, who in turn put me in touch with the manager of the camp at Bognor Regis, and all along I received nothing but helpfulness and genuine concern and was immensely grateful for that chance meeting with Sir William. An arrangement was made for me to visit the site at Bognor Regis, and after a thorough inspection of the camp the manager took me to an area where he felt the proposed centre should be located. However, whilst I thought it important that the patients and their families should be part of a real holiday scene, somehow I could not picture them responding happily to the noise and bustle which were part and parcel of any lively holiday camp. The excited screams of the children, mingled with the whine of the go-carts, against a background of a gay and friendly voice announcing the start of an archery competition seemed too much! I felt that what the patients really needed was a quiet and peaceful atmosphere where there were facilities to be enjoyed if the mood was right, and I shared my thinking with the kindly manager. He understood immediately and suggested that I should contact a man called Ken Newington, who had recently sold his two holiday villages to the Butlin group but who was still employed as Chairman on a service contract at the Sussex Beach Holiday Village near Bracklesham Bay on the West Sussex coast.

Ken Newington welcomed me with open arms, as if he had been waiting all these years for just such a project to be put to him, and without a moment's hesitation offered me the car park in the middle of the holiday village as a suitable site on which to build our centre. It was just exactly what I was looking for and excitement ran high as I considered the implications of my plan. A modular building was the obvious choice since it was not only cheaper, but quicker, to erect and had the undoubted advantage of being portable and, therefore, would find the ready approval of the county planners. I tentatively approached one of my friends at Guy's Hospital and invited both him and the senior nurse to advise me on the setting up of what, in essence, was a small renal unit. I shared my excitement with a few carefully chosen sympathetic renal consultants, who seemed as delighted as I that their patients at last would be able to enjoy a holiday like the rest of us. My initial idea was to equip the centre to enable four patients to be dialysed at a time, and to loan it that first year to renal units all over the country who would send their patients, together with their own nurses, from one unit at a time to avoid cross-infection with patients from other groups. I would also employ a technician who would be in charge of the ordering of supplies, guarding our interests and giving help when it was needed. I knew I should need a man in charge, and who better than my old friend Doug Farrend from the Portsmouth days, who had taught me all I knew about dialysis. Doug had retired from St Mary's and was, I felt, more than happy to come out of his retirement and face a new challenge.

Shopping for the centre brought me some of the happiest hours of my life. Having visited a number of holiday dialysis caravans, chalets, and Portakabins, I knew exactly what it was I should *not* do. I was determined that our holiday centre would be a home from home, as far removed from a hospital atmosphere as was practically possible. Everywhere the head turned the eye fell on evidence of love and caring: I threw myself with excitement into making the centre warm and welcoming, sparing nothing in effort but ensuring that no purchase was made without a generous discount. I bought Parker Knoll reclining chairs covered in bright blue rexine – no patient on holiday was going to dialyse in a bed! Gay floral curtains and pictures on the walls immediately gave the room a homely look, and would hopefully help to allay the apprehension of visiting patients who were dialysing in a strange place for the first time. Toasters, sandwich makers, microwave ovens, television sets, and video games were bought with money sent in by kind and generous people who all wanted to be part of the new scheme.

Portakabin, in less time than it took to say 'rabbit', had build a magnificent place for us which, together with the treatment room, included a large kitchen, WC, store-room, and hall. Much to their chagrin, or even possible horror, I set about disguising the fact that the building was a Portakabin! I had it painted white with blue shutters and a blue trellis and built a little porch over the front door on which were written the words 'The Grove'. Some months before the centre was built Mary Graves, the daughter of the Chairman of Wimpey, had heard of my work and been in touch with me offering financial support. When the building was complete and the bills unpaid, I went to see her and asked her if she felt she would like to pay them, and her immediate reply was 'yes'. Mary was the Trustee of 'The Grove Family Trust', so I named our first centre out of gratitude to her.

With a promise from Ken Newington that no charge would be made for water or electricity, with all bills paid by Mary Graves, and with Doug Farrend at the helm we were ready to go. The evening before we opened our doors to the first patients we got together with a bottle of champagne provided by Ken and drank a toast to the future success of the centre and the happiness and well-being of the patients. I was excited beyond imagination at the realization of a dream. There I was standing in the first holiday dialysis centre of its kind in the country, waiting to spread happiness and freedom to people who had been denied it for so long. There was my old friend and supporter Doug, who had witnessed so much of our personal suffering and was now with me, waiting to prove that so often out of evil can come good and out of sorrow can come happiness.

The first visitors that summer in 1980 were four children from a London paediatric unit but their visit, far from being a source of joy to me, proved a shattering experience. The young patients themselves were so thrilled to be on holiday, but instead of coming with their families, whom I had expected to take accommodation in the holiday village, with the nurses simply there to dialyse them, they came along with a veritable retinue of medical staff. A teacher, a dietitian, a young foreign doctor, a nursing Sister, and three nurses – I was dismayed. The whole object of my plan was to offer a real holiday to the patients and their families to help combat the isolation that so many of them feel and to bring normality back into their lives. These children, surrounded as they were by medical, nursing, and teaching staff, had not the smallest chance of being, or feeling, like normal, healthy children; dialysis was being made the focal point of their lives and I could have wept with disappointment.

There were other problems, too. I had been assured by the

consultant at the very hospital from which these children came that if I did not insist on signed certificates being sent in advance of the patients, certifying that they were not carriers of the serum hepatitis which was the dread of all renal physicians, I could never hope for support for the centre. These patients arrived without their certificates and the failure was immediately reported to me by Doug. The senior sister assured him that all the patients were A.A. negative, but we had made rules at their own hospital's suggestion and I intended that we would adhere to them. I told Doug that one of the nurses must drive back to the London unit, returning with the certificates, and that until we had seen them he was not to open the centre for dialysis. The senior sister was furious and refused to send one of her nurses. Her decision was upheld, much to my amazement, by the paediatric nephrologist in London who angrily told me that I was making a fuss about nothing and his word should be sufficient.

At the end of the two-week stay Doug Ferrend reported miserably to me that the nurses had treated the place as if it were their own, had completely ignored him, were discourteous and hurtful, and that if the next batch of patients visiting the following fortnight were to bring with them nurses with the same attitude and of the same calibre, he would give in his notice. To add insult to injury, on their departure they had dumped six black bags of rubbish outside my beautiful holiday dialysis centre, in which I took such pride, which incurred not only my wrath but the anger and consternation of the holiday camp manager. It was a very bad start, which I found most discouraging, but it served only to strengthen my determination that in the future I would run the centre myself with our own nurses, hoping gradually to build up the confidence of the renal consultants by adhering strictly to the rules that I had been urged to make.

Although we were not fully booked that first season, a number of units from all over the country took advantage of the facilities that I offered and, on my part, I gleaned much valuable information which was to stand me in good stead as we welcomed more and more patients in the years ahead.

In my anxiety to acquaint myself more fully with the problems encountered by the patients and their families I sought every opportunity to visit renal units and talk with the consultants and the nursing staff. I had become increasingly concerned by the attitudes of some of the renal units towards the patients and their families. From my stand point, I viewed the patient with the utmost sympathy and compassion. Here was a man or woman who, through no fault of their own, was condemned to life on a kidney machine with the intermittent reprieve that transplantation brought them. People who once walked tall in the community and pulled their weight, who held down decent jobs, were real lovers to their spouse and parents to their children, had become half-people, and were well aware of it. Jobs were lost, mortgages and domestic bills could no longer be paid, rough-housing with the children had become fun of the past, tempers were frayed, libido was reduced, and all in all the patients painted for me a picture so overwhelmingly poignant that my only wish was to help them in their plight. The same emotions were not always forthcoming from some of the renal consultants and the nurses in charge of the patients' medical care.

Even in the best units, where the consultants and, therefore, the nursing staff viewed the patient with compassion, even there real understanding was often lacking. A weekly or fortnightly meeting of all the members of the team concerned with the patient's welfare, including the social worker, was held to discuss each patient's case. On occasions even in these units, when a home patient had been admitted overloaded after an outburst of dietary indiscretion, for example, the attitude was unsympathetic in the extreme, and the patient was left in no doubt as to the additional trouble his admission had caused, incurring the unkind disapproval of the whole team. Such outbursts were often a *cri de coeur* which passed unnoticed by those in charge. Whilst I appreciated the difficulties confronting both doctors and the nursing staff I felt that more effort should be made to understand the patient's point of view. Other relatives like myself have encountered great difficulties with a patient who, for example, having received his transplant call finds, on arrival at the hospital, that the relatives have changed their minds at the last moment and have decided not to donate their loved one's kidneys. This crushing blow was struck twice at Timbo, and on each occasion he threw caution to the winds and, flatly refusing to adhere to his restricted fluid intake, drank himself nearly into the grave. So often these indiscretions were a sign that the patient was no longer prepared to accept the restrictions on his life and would rather run the risk of losing it.

I suppose it is the lot of all chronic patients that they should feel sometimes that their entire life has been taken over by the doctors concerned with their care. The renal patients dependent on dialysis or transplantation feel this more strongly than other patients with a chronic disability or illness. Perhaps it is the need for constant medical supervision that makes the doctor feel he has the right to dictate the life of his patients outside the clinic. It seemed to me that, providing the patient's behaviour did not threaten the welfare and health of his fellow patients and those medical and nursing staff looking after him, what he chose to do with his own life should be his own affair, but, for example, both the doctors and the nursing staff were often particularly scathing of the non-working patient who had received a transplant and took the attitude illustrated in the remark once made to me by a transplant surgeon: 'I don't know why we bothered with him. He flatly refuses to go back to work!'

The very idea that consideration should be given to the *worth* of a renal patient requiring treatment is incredible when consideration is given to the thousands of apparently utterly useless alcoholics and drug addicts who naturally, and quite rightly, are treated time and time again without any thought being given by the doctors as to whether or not the patient was worthy of the trouble and expense.

There also seemed to be too little understanding of the self-discipline required by the patients adhering to their strict diet and fluid intake, and that they were able to steer a reasonably steady course in these matters was cause for congratulation, and not remonstration if they found the course too steep. The renal unit staff, who were always overworked and often harassed, obviously found it difficult to appreciate the problems faced by the average dialysis patient. I remember once standing in a renal unit chatting to the Sister at the end of the day shift when one of the chronic night patients appeared on the ward. He walked slowly to his allotted bed looking neither to the right nor to the left and the expression of dull acceptance on his drawn face provoked a stern, uncaring rebuke from the Sister.

'When you come into this ward, Mr Hughes, you might at least have the courtesy to smile and say good evening. I don't know why you should think you have cause to look like that.'

Why indeed! No doubt Mr Hughes, with great effort, had managed to get through his day's work and at the end, when one of his mates turned to him and said, 'Coming along to the Blue Bell tonight, Jim?' his reply would have been, 'No, sorry, I have to go and dialyse.'

Sister, who had been involved all day with the dialysis of a new and difficult patient beset by many medical complications, seeing the reproachful expression on my face explained: 'They sometimes make me angry. If they saw what went on in this ward during the daytime they would realize how lucky there were to be a fit and normal dialysis patient.'

I told her that I thought no dialysis patient saw himself as normal since it was not normal to be a dialysis patient, and that the resentment that they so often felt because of their condition was surely understandable and, therefore, should be acceptable.

Another area that also gave me cause for great concern was the proprietary attitude that many of the paediatric renal consultants and their nursing staff had towards their young patients. They were treated almost like dolls or puppets, encouraged in their dependence on the unit staff, jealously guarded from strangers or other agencies wishing to help them and bring them happiness, and in some units, far from being encouraged to grow up and join their peers, they were actively discouraged from seeking a world outside the renal unit. Many of these children were undersized and under-developed – the boys with male voices as yet unbroken – so that young adults in their late teens appeared as children of ten or twelve. I have actually witnessed a youth of seventeen, with a shock of blonde hair and a round baby face, sitting on Sister's lap being jogged up and down on her knee like a three-year-old baby. I certainly understood the difficulties facing the nursing staff, many of whom had been in at the beginning and fought long and hard to get the child established on dialysis and to overcome all the medical and emotional problems involved, but they should have under-stood – or perhaps it should have been pointed out to them – the damage they were doing in retarding the developent of the very children that they so obviously cared for.

I have tried over the years, without success, to encourage renal paediatric nephrologists to allow some of their teenage patients to make up a party and go on holiday at our holiday dialysis centre at Sussex Beach, where their dialysis would be taken care of and where they would be independent of adults and able to notch up a few private experiences of their own. The transition from child to adult is difficult for everyone but for the young, growing renal patient whose life revolves around dialysis in the hospital or in the home it is even harder. Unfortunately there were no adolescent dialysis units because of the shortage of facilities, so there were no opportunities for the thirteen and fourteen year olds to let go of the hand of the paediatric nephrologist and leave behind them the pictures of Noddy on the unit walls to move into a dignified atmosphere more suited to their age. Either they were in the children's unit, where they were being fussed over and spoilt, or they were transferred to the adult unit where their young needs could not be properly catered for. Many of

them consequently did not leave the paediatric unit until they
were in their late teens or early twenties and, as a result, they
found it harder to accept the inevitable break with the renal
unit through transplantation and the realities of adulthood.
There was never any doubt in my mind about the genuine
love and concern felt for these young patients by the nursing
staff, but whilst the patients quite naturally depended on
them it seemed that the nurses often felt the same dependence
and were reluctant to let them go.

The not-so-good units were very easy to recognize. These
units were (and some are still today) run like a dictatorship by
the renal consultant in charge, who saw no reason for weekly
staff meetings where the team could get together and discuss
each patient's needs and problems, and who very often
refused the services of a renal social worker and discouraged
all contact with the BKPA. They strutted around their
kingdoms like tin gods and caused much unhappiness, not
only amongst their patients but also amongst the staff. On
reading through letters written to me by distressed patients or
their relatives I became quite expert at recognizing which unit
was in charge of the patient's treatment. Many of the patients
and their families travelled long distances to seek my advice
and support and, whilst they knew they had a strong ally and
a good friend in me, I was always careful to remind them of
the need for diplomacy since to antagonize their consultant
would simply make matters worse for them.

I once received a telephone call from a social worker,
working in one of these units, who wanted to arrange a
clandestine meeting at a local hotel to share with me her
concern for the welfare of her clients. She knew that if the
consultant was aware of our meeting it would be made more
difficult for her to help the patients, but I was horrified to
realize that the consultant wielded such power over the unit
staff that such extreme measures were thought to be
necessary. Apparently the heartless behaviour of the
consultant towards his patients was upsetting the staff, who
felt unable to intervene on the patients' behalf. Naturally they

were afraid of losing their jobs, so rather than risk a confrontation with the consultant the social worker had decided to seek my advice. I said that I thought that her duty lay with her clients and that both she and the home dialysis administrator, who had turned up at the meeting feeling equally concerned and unhappy, should confront the consultant with their complaints, demanding a change in his behaviour and attitudes, or they would resign. They both thought my advice was too drastic to be acceptable and although I commiserated with them both, I was surprised that they were prepared to continue to work under such appalling conditions. The renal consultant of that unit is still in charge today, and continues to deny his patients the freedom and understanding that they so richly deserve. He has made it known that I would not be welcome to visit his unit but, perhaps unbeknown to him, the social worker continues to refer the patients in need and I continue to help them.

It was difficult to believe that in this wonderful country of ours there really were patients being denied treatment, not because treatment was unknown, but because no treatment was made available for them. It has been said that there are a few cases where dialysis, because of multi-system disease, could be felt unsuitable for a patient. Undoubtedly the treatment would prolong the patient's life, but the trauma and discomfort caused to the patient, already terminally ill from other causes, might reasonably be thought to be adding an unnecessary burden both to the patient and his family.

However, as it has been the practice over the years to withhold, both from the patient and his relatives, the truth behind the refusal to offer dialysis treatment, there have been a variety of reasons thought up by the renal consultants and their team to justify their decision not to treat.

Patients are today being denied treatment because of their age, social conditions, or through language barriers, because they suffer from diabetes or are paraplegics or spina bifidas, because they have no partner to help them with home dialysis, or no home suitable for the treatment to be carried out in, and on the grounds that the quality of life offered to a patient on dialysis would be unacceptable to the patient himself. I have always felt very strongly that only an individual has the right to decide on the quality of his life and that no man has the right to make that decision for another unless he is mentally incapable of making the decision himself. Patients at that time, and unfortunately now, were being selected out of treatment on the grounds that the quality of life offered to the patient on dialysis would not warrant the expense. Sadly, in an ideal world where money was no object and facilities were available for all who needed them, no consultant would need to select patients out of treatment for the reasons given today, and certainly no honest consultant could find justification for refusing to treat.

There have been times, of course, when a renal physician has found himself in a genuine dilemma and one such case I recall vividly. I received a telephone call one afternoon from a young man called Smith, whose mother had been admitted to a local hospital in end-stage renal failure. The hospital in question did not have a renal unit but did have emergency facilities in the form of a peritoneal dialysis machine, and the patient had been placed on dialysis in a holding situation whilst her doctor made contact with the consultant at the nearest renal unit. The renal consultant was short of facilities at that time and made the decision not to accept the forty-five-year-old patient on to his programme for two good reasons. Firstly, he was unable to offer her long-term hospital dialysis and he felt that as her husband was a non-English speaking Pole, although she herself was English, home dialysis would not be suitable. Secondly, a short period of hospital dialysis followed by early transplantation was, in his opinion, out of the question as she had an ulcerated leg condition which would have been aggravated by the steroids that she would have been required to take in order to prevent the new kidney from rejecting. It is conceivable that the patient, had she been asked, would have preferred to have taken the chance of losing a leg in return for her life but, of course, she was not made aware of the true situation and nor, indeed, were her sons. With the death sentence pronounced by the visiting consultant, the problem left to the local doctors was how to carry it out.

Peritoneal dialysis is a method of cleaning the blood whereby the patient's own peritoneum is used as the dialyser and dialysis fluid is fed into the peritoneum by a tube and drained out again, taking with it the poisons and extra fluid accumulated in the blood. The patient naturally, as a result of this process, feels considerably better than before – when the kidneys have ceased to function the blood becomes full of poisons and the body bloated with fluid, and consequently the patient feels desperately ill. So it was in the case of the Smith boy's mother, when one of her sons called me at my office and asked for my advice and help.

'It's too terrible, Mrs Ward, but my mother is feeling better now than she has felt for a long time, walking about the ward and chatting and smiling with us and the other patients.'

He was obviously anxious but I failed to understand. 'What is so terrible, Mr Smith?'

'She keeps asking why they are not changing her dialysis bags. She is worried they have stopped treating her, and so am I.'

I tried to reassure him by telling him that I was quite sure no doctor would allow, let alone recommend, the cessation of treatment of a patient who was walking around the ward chatting and laughing and in full control of her senses. There must be some mistake, I said.

'No, Mrs Ward,' he replied. 'That was several days ago that she was so well and happy. Now she is quite different. For the last two days when meals are brought to the other patients my mother is left out and instead of being given food, which she asks for because she says she is hungry, a nurse comes and gives her an injection. After a bit she gets drowsy and does not seem to know what she is saying and won't talk to us any more.'

I knew that this boy understood what they were doing to his mother at the hospital but he could not bring himself to say the words. I could imagine the scene, the embarrassing questions asked of the nurses by a friendly, talkative patient feeling better than she had felt for weeks. How do you discontinue treatment of someone who has their wits about them and suspects the worse? The only way is to dim their powers of concentration, cut down their awareness, and destroy their minds; hence the need for regular injections.

I felt sick inside as I rang the renal consultant to try to get to the bottom of this horrifying tale. He was utterly truthful and told me that, of course, if facilities had been available for him to take this patient onto his chronic hospital programme there was no doubt in his mind that the patient's life would be saved.

'I'm going to give this one to the press, Tony. Do you agree with that?' I asked. 'And will you tell the press what you have told me, because we really cannot have a situation where doctors are actually slowly killing people because there are not enough facilities to treat them.'

Tony gave me his assurance, without hesitation, that should the press get in touch with him he would tell them the truth because he himself regretted very much what he called 'the turn of events'. (Strangely enough, despite his genuine concern and anger, it had apparently never entered his head to contact one of his colleagues with a view to getting this patient treated elsewhere.)

I was in constant touch with both the patient's sons during the days that it took their mother to die, but felt powerless to do anything to help. Why I did not get into my car and drive post-haste to the hospital where this wretched woman lay dying I cannot to this day understand, but I did not and I feel that I contributed to her death. I had been alerted to the awfulness of what was happening whilst there was still time to help, but whereas today I would not hesitate to confront a doctor who had ordered the death of a patient no matter what the reason, in those days I was not so confident of my position when it came to interfering in what were cleverly termed 'medical decisions'.

I spoke on a radio programme with both of the patient's sons a few days after her death, decrying the present situation and using them as an example of the suffering caused not only to the patients but those that loved them. The consultant, of course, was never given the opportunity of voicing his own protest through the media since the hospital administrator took all press calls and persistently repeated the lie, 'We have no shortage of facilities at this hospital and the decision not to give dialysis treatment to the patient was based entirely on her medical condition.' The hospital authorities had no intention of risking the inevitable criticisms.

All too often the decision, apparently based on the quality of life, to terminate or deny treatment was made not with the happiness and well-being of the patient in mind but for the convenience of the doctors and nursing staff. There were two horrific examples which had been drawn to my attention by the summer of 1980. I was invited to attend the fortnightly meeting held by the consultant in charge of the renal unit, together with the transplant team, at a renal unit north of the Thames. I listened with interest to the discussion concerning each individual patient and their prospects of a successful transplant. The consultant physician rose to his feet and, walking towards a list of names, pinned to the wall, he invited the transplant surgeon to join him. With a pencil held in his right hand, he went slowly down the list of names, saying to the transplant surgeon: 'I'll have him, and him, and her, not her; I'll take him, not her, not him,' and so on until he had arrived at the end of the list. I asked the meaning of this puzzling selection and was told that there were certain patients who were now on dialysis whom the consultant physician was not prepared to take back onto dialysis if their transplants failed. Further enquiries showed that, facilities being short, selection was inevitably being practised, and that the patients for whom the renal physicians had donned the black cap were patients who, for one reason or another, had 'not found dialysis acceptable'. This confirmed my worst fears. It appeared that the patient's unwillingness to accept further dialysis after a failed transplant was illustrated by his behaviour, not by his expressed wish. These patients were disruptive on the ward, upsetting to the other patients and nursing staff, displayed a truculent and uncooperative attitude, and by their constant complaining and refusal to adhere to the rigid diet and fluid intake they had unknowingly earned themselves the death sentence.

An actual example of this terrifying situation was brought to my attention that summer and a call was put through to me in my office from a thirty-eight-year-old woman who told me that her husband's transplant had failed and she had been told that further dialysis was not to be offered him.

'Please, please, Mrs Ward, try and save my husband's life. I believe he only has a few days to live.'

Apparently she had asked the consultant why her husband could not be put back on dialysis, as she knew that there was no shortage of facilities in this particular unit, where her husband had not long since been dialysing, at that time. She was told by the consultant that her husband's medical condition did not warrant further treatment on dialysis and, despite her persistent pleading to allow her husband to go back on the machine once more, the consultant remained firm. She herself was unconvinced that her husband would not respond to treatment, but felt that the reason for the refusal to offer him further treatment lay in the fact that he was forty-two years old with no dependants, since she herself was working and they were a childless couple.

I was fortunate in being able to find the consultant in his office and, telling him of my recent conversation with his patient's wife, I asked whether the patient had some sinister medical condition unbeknown to his wife which could account for his decision not to place his patient back on the machine.

'Indeed not,' he said, 'but he is not the sort of patient we like to have up here. He is a trouble-maker and so, indeed, is his wife; a very difficult couple to deal with, constantly causing disruption on the ward. You know the sort of person, always insisting on his rights; very difficult to deal with indeed.'

I expressed my horror and consternation in no uncertain terms, and the consultant then went on to explain that, 'We can do nothing with him since he refuses to comply with our regime and frequently turns up late for dialysis, causing havoc on the ward and disrupting our routine.'

There seemed no question of the consultant making arrangements for the patient to be taken on to the programme of another renal unit that specialized in home dialysis since either that thought had not entered his head or he was not prepared to pass his problems onto one of his colleagues. I called the patient's wife and told her some of my conversation, and added, 'I can do nothing to save his life but I promise you that he will not die in vain.' Five days later I managed to arrange for her to talk on a national radio programme, by which time she was a widow.

I could not then accept or understand, and I cannot now, the unique attitude on the part of renal consultants who persistently conceal the truth from their patients and those that love them, thus denying the opportunity of seeking help elsewhere and, at the same time, shouldering unnecessarily the full responsibility for their patient's death. The shortage of dialysis facilities is the responsibility of the National Health Service and not the consultant, and it seemed to me that until the responsibility could be placed firmly where it belonged, no more facilities would be forthcoming.

# 7

# A Change for the Better

Meanwhile, there had been changes in the BKPA. On 30 June 1978 I had said goodbye to my beloved friend, Robert Platt. After attending a meeting at the Royal College of Physicians in London earlier that month he suffered what was to prove a fatal accident. He tripped at the stop of the steps and fell to the bottom, causing multiple fractures to his legs. I visited him in hospital a few days after the accident, just two days before his death, and realized that I was going to lose a much-loved and trusted friend. I not only grieved with, but for, his lovely wife Sylvia, who was many years his junior and was left with her two beautiful daughters to face life without him.

When I had recovered sufficiently from Robert's death to consider a replacement sponsor for the Association, I invited Lord Hunt of Fawley to take his place. John Hunt was a GP of renown, with a large and wealthy practice in Sloane Street, who was highly thought of by his colleagues and seemed pleased to accept my invitation. I had assumed that with his wide experience of general practice he would be of invaluable help to me in my work, but alas that was not to be. In the early days he was too busy to involve himself with our specialized problems and later he was tragically struck down by blindness, forcing him into early retirement and resignation from sponsorship of the BKPA. I decided that one sponsor was sufficient, as Trevor Huddleston was still playing an active part in the work of the Association, turning up at all meetings, and showing genuine concern for the plight of the patients and interest in my work.

Until then we had had no patron. I had never thought it necessary to have royal patronage although, of course, it would have been wonderful had it come my way. A non-royal patron did not seem to me to be either necessary or appropriate, so I surprised myself by making an unexpected decision to invite the Duke of Westminster to be our patron. I thought it would be nice to have the interest and support of a young man of Timbo's age – and he was, in fact both at Sunningdale prep school with him and at Harrow, where they were in the same house together. Obviously Gerald's name as Duke of Westminster had some standing, although, contrary to popular belief, I did not think for one moment that his patronage of my Association would mean the end of my need to fund raise! I wrote to Gerald asking him if he would like to be patron of the BKPA and he replied that he would be delighted. He paid his first official visit to the headquarters one summer afternoon and, much to the delight of my staff, arrived by helicopter and landed in the donkey's field in time for lunch! His youthful vigour and genuine enthusiasm for hard work, added to his business acumen, have proved of great benefit to me over the years but he never opened the door to the vaults of the Bank of England nor even led me to believe that his friends could be used as a passport to easy fund raising, and in this I have been neither surprised nor disappointed.

I had also changed some of my original Council members, asking them if they would be prepared to resign since a little criticism had been levelled at the fact that all the experts on my Council were based in London! The first good friend to go was Professor Martin Barratt, the paediatric nephrologist working at the Hospital for Sick Children, Great Ormond Street, who very kindly agreed to stand down for his colleague, Dick White, who was attached to the Children's Hospital, Birmingham. Professor Roy Calne, the surgeon who pioneered renal transplants in this country and who was working at Addenbrooke's Hospital, Cambridge, was one of the first serving members on my Council, but unfortunately he and I fell out on a matter of policy in the early days and since we could obviously never work together as we were pulling in opposite directions, he resigned. His place was taken by Robert Sells, the transplanter at Liverpool, which gave us representation further up the map.

Roy and I fell out over the matter of patient participation. I had founded an Association for the benefit of kidney patients and I knew from my own experience that the kidney patient himself was not the best person to fight for his own rights. He was entirely dependent on his renal unit for his life and was well aware of it, and he knew that any criticism that might reflect on the renal unit staff would prove unpopular and embarrassing. Quite apart from the geographical complications of involvement with the BKPA, housed as it was in my country home in Hampshire, it seemed untenable that patients themselves should be involved in discussions which might well undermine the confidence they had not only in their own doctors, but in the system as a whole. Also, I felt sure that with patients present at meetings many important matters which should come under discussion would be avoided by the doctors, partly out of consideration for the patients and partly because they were not used to discussing certain matters in front of the patients themselves. Roy disagreed, and wanted patient participation.

When the Association was founded we had agreed that Council meetings would be an annual event, and it did seem to me that, with six or seven months' advance warning and a choice of several dates, it should have been possible for us to have managed to meet together once a year. There was, however, not one single occasion from the date of inauguration until 1984 when all the Council members were present together at our Annual General Meeting. I gradually realized, of course, that the problem was the measure of the importance – or lack of it – that they themselves placed on the work of the Association and the value of the discussions that took place at the meetings.

As the years progressed I was becoming more and more concerned about the attitude of the consultants and the treatment of the patients and their families, and quite obviously my Council found these discussions embarrassing. They refused point-blank to involve themselves in the shortcomings of their colleagues, although they were always able *in camera* to recognize and acknowledge the criticisms. I certainly understood their point of view and found it easy to forgive their attitude of *laissez-faire* since, of course, they had to work with their colleagues, but I could not forgive their lack of attendance at meetings and discussed the problem one day with my patron, Gerald Westminster. He thought it was high time that I took up a new broom and swept clean. His own feelings were that I should dissolve the present Council, which was made up entirely of members of the medical profession, and broaden its base. The new Council should include only one member of the medical profession, the others being chosen from the world of commerce and finance – people with good connections, time on their hands, and true dedication to the cause. Gerald also told me that he would very much like to give up patronage of the Association and serve on the Council himself. I was eager to accept this offer, and also his suggestion that there should be a biannual meeting of the Council – which should be held in London, for everyone's convenience, and not at head office in Hampshire.

Whilst these changes were being considered it seemed an ideal opportunity to review the whole structure of the Association, and after some consideration I decided to delegate the task of grant making and form a Grants Committee. Hitherto the Council of Management had been responsible not only for policy making but also for the distribution of our funds to worthwhile projects, leaving me in charge of the daily running of the Association – which included the dispensing of funds to cover the needs of the patients. Under the chairmanship of my old friend Dr David Kerr, who had left renal medicine to become Dean of the Hammersmith Hospital, I gathered together a team of renal consultants well known to me, and well loved, who were eminently capable of deciding between them which grant application was worthy of support and which was not.

Never being one for working in committee myself, I decided to keep the new Council small and manageable and in addition to myself, Gerald Westminster and Stewart Cameron, a professor of renal medicine at Guy's Hospital, who had served on my Council since inauguration, only two more names were added to the list of Council members. With a certain amount of difficulty I persuaded Christopher Weatherby, the Chairman of Weatherby, the administrators of horse racing for the Jockey Club, to join us, not only because he was a friend of long standing and had much experience to bring to the conference table, but because as a relative of a kidney patient he understood so well the problems confronting them. Johnnie Milln, recently retired senior partner of Savory Milln, the city stockbrokers, opened up a whole new field of fund raising when he became the fifth member of the new Council of Management. Who better to help me in my endless efforts to increase the fortunes of the BKPA than these three captains of industry and finance, and who better able to direct the flow of our joint efforts than five of the top consultants in the renal world?

The need for fund raising was ever present and sometimes I was haunted by the fear that some national or international disaster would occur, presenting a need greater than our own. Whilst the fund stood at well over £1 million by the beginning of 1980, our commitments were constantly increasing, and although our overheads had been kept to the minimum, the demands on our limited resources were sometimes alarming. I had resisted all tempting approaches from fund-raising experts in the belief that if they felt they could raise the money that I needed then surely so could I, and far more cheaply! I had established the Association on a very personal basis, not because I had sought the publicity for myself, but because I knew that the personal angle was the one most likely to produce results. I was not only the founder and President of the Association, but the mother of a kidney patient, who had experienced many problems and much of the anguish, and, therefore, attracted a great deal of personal sympathy.

Although I had not realized it, people had taken note of the fact that I worked for love, not salary. I was in a fortunate position to be able to enjoy the privileges and luxury life-style that a brilliant husband had bestowed on me, without having to work the long, hard hours that I did. That in itself, I now know, engendered in people a real wish to help and be identified with the task I had set myself.

No matter what request I was making I always wrote directly to the potential donor, bypassing equerries, private secretaries, junior ministers, and cutting through the protective barrier. I knew, of course, that they had first sight of letters addressed to Heads and Secretaries of State, royalty, and sometimes even opera singers, but I knew also that they were duty-bound to discuss the contents of the letter, if it was personally addressed, with their lord and master. Many people have speculated, and asked me directly, how on earth I was able to gather together such a galaxy of stars year after year at my carol concerts at St Peter's, Eaton Square. The answer was I simply wrote and asked them. I knew that there was a need, and that the need was real, and whilst of course, I realized that there were many other needy causes to support, to me, at least, mine seemed the most deserving. I think I might have been fortunate in the turn of phrase I used when writing but I wrote from the heart, and when I began a letter, 'I am writing to you because I desperately need your help', I wrote that because I was desperate for the help that I was asking for.

So it was when I set about the task of putting together an interesting selection of items for the BKPA Charity Sale to be held at Sotheby's galleries on 6 October 1980, and this gave me something to take my mind off the prospect of the September transplant operation. Every item was an outright donation but the work involved in gathering together the minimum of seventy-four articles required to make an evening Charity Sale was formidable. Timbo had long since left Sotheby's but I had kept up my contacts and, in some cases, friendships with a few of the directors and staff. Sir Philip Hay, a director of Sotheby's was a staunch supporter and it did not, therefore, prove too difficult to enlist their help. The director detailed to oversee the sale was not a personal friend and during the months we worked together he came no nearer to becoming one! He was used to working with fine art in an atmosphere where thirteenth-century Chinese porcelain plates were used as ashtrays and he was convinced my efforts to secure similar items for the sale were doomed from the start. He knew where he was with titles and million-dollar notes but he was certainly at sea with me, an excited, enthusiastic, country bumpkin who had neither. The fact that my enthusiasm was not shared made life more difficult but increased my determination to make the sale a success.

The Order of St John had been the charity to benefit from the previous annual Charity Sale and fortunately my old friend, Lady Wilkinson, had been the organizer. I invited Sylvia to lunch in the hope of getting a few tips and with the idea of discussing the implications of my commitment. We met together in April, only six months before the sale, and before she had even finished her drink she was assuring me of failure or worse. 'You must be crazy,' she said. 'You cannot possibly arrange an important sale at Sotheby's with only a few months to go when you have not even got one single item given you. You have no idea of what is involved in collecting together things of worth and you have not even got a committee.'

I told her lamely that whilst it was true I had not actually any items for sale in my possession I had had promises.

'Well, what sort of things have you been promised and who has promised them?' she asked.

'Well, the Queen is giving me a pair of silver-plated goblets; Prince Michael of Kent is giving me a pair of riding boots; the Duke of Gloucester a beautiful book; the Prime Minister has promised me a Spode plate; and young Winston Churchill is giving me the overcoat which his grandfather wore on budget day in 1926. The Princess Royal and the Prince of Wales have both made donations, so I have got some support.'

When I finally drew breath I was gratified to see that the expression on her face had changed! She was a wonderful help to me and it was nice to have someone who had participated in a previous Charity Sale to talk things over with although, of course, hers was on a much grander scale.

I felt that the importance of my sale would rest not with what I had been given but on who had given it to me, and that was the theme I finally settled on. Needless to say Sylvia was there on the night giving me much-needed support and, bless her heart, adding her name to the long list of buyers. By the beginning of July I had done the rounds of Buckingham Palace, Kensington Palace, Downing Street, and Chester Street, and less fashionable addresses, and had gathered together quite a presentable collection of items to be entered in the sale and these were delivered to Sotheby's for safe keeping whilst I set about adding to my hoard. Having written to all my friends and acquaintances and a fair number of complete strangers whom I felt might be worth an approach, I was left with no alternative but to adopt the representatives' 'cold call'. Several days a week, when work at my office was organized, I drove to London comfortably shod in flat shoes and trod the West End calling on jewellers, fine art dealers, and picture galleries, explaining my need and the purpose of my visit to any director or manager prepared to listen. People were amazingly generous and understanding and although in the time it took to make each call and complete each interview I could have signed my name to several dozen letters, I felt not one call was wasted and only seldom did I come away empty-handed or without the promise of help in the future.

I was afraid that my friendly director at Sotheby's was unimpressed by the results of my labours and had, I was sure, privately decided to spend as little of his valuable time as possible on what to him was a second-class effort but to me was one of the highlights of my fund-raising career. Certainly very little advance publicity had been given to the forthcoming sale and I must admit to having been disappointed at the small attendance, noting that most of those present were drawn from the ranks of my own friends. I was also so sad not to have been able to share that evening with either of my two men, since Timbo was still in hospital recovering from the after-effects of receiving his father's kidney and Nigel was not yet fully recovered from having given it. There were many unusual items for sale that night but none more unusual than a half share in a nomination to Ile de Bourbon, which had been arranged for me through the British Bloodstock Agency by David McCall. The nomination was sold for £20,000, of which the BKPA received half. It was not possible to sell the nomination at auction that night, but our share of the proceeds from the sale went towards the final total which was in the region of £30,000.

It seemed such a little time after the sale was over that I was turning my attention once more to the problem of the shortage of facilities for patients in need of dialysis and transplantation. I was well satisfied with our first season at our holiday dialysis centre near Bracklesham Bay. The modular building erected by Portakabin in a matter of three weeks with facilities for four patients proved eminently suitable for the job of dialysing eight patients a week. I had been able to produce a realistic costing which compared favourably with the dialysis costing given by the DHSS and it seemed to me that if the Regional Health Authorities could be persuaded to set up small, economic satellite dialysis units in their regions, dialysis could be undertaken at a very much lower rate than was currently the case, and as a result more patients could be taken on to the programme and more lives saved. I had suggested to the Minister of Health, Dr Gerard Vaughan (now Sir Gerard), earlier in the summer that he might himself write a letter to the thirteen Regional Chairmen calling their attention to the considerable savings that the BKPA had been able to make and urging them to follow our example.

Gerry Vaughan, who seemed to think I was a good thing – or was, in any case, clever enough to allow me to think so – was genuinely open to any suggestion that might improve the current situation without extra cash having to be found. At one of our monthly meetings I discussed the possibility of having an exhibition unit on display in London, open to inspection by the Regional Health Authority Chairmen and renal physicians so that they would be in a position to assess the value for themselves. Gerry thought that the idea was an excellent one and agreed to write round to all the RHA Chairmen, and also to open the exhibition for me. Encouraged by his cooperation I approached the Ministry of Works for permission to site my exhibition on the Foreign Office Green. I was told that the normal duration of an exhibition on that site was forty-eight hours and my request for a longer period would have to be given special consideration by a higher authority. I seem to remember that the Keeper of the Royal Parks was involved in the actual decision to grant me my request. There was to be no charge made – even for the electricity supply which, to my delight, came from Number 10 Downing Street! I was much amused to learn that when an application had been made by the Ministry of Works to Number 10 for permission to connect to their supply, this conversation took place.

'How long for, then, the usual forty-eight hours?'

'No,' came the reply. 'Six weeks.'

'Six weeks! Who on earth has got it for that length of time?'

'The BKPA.'

'Oh well,' came the retort, 'that explains it!'

Portakabin, who were cooperating to the full, appreciating the wonderful publicity that the exhibition offered them, had already despatched the building by road from York and once again all charges were waived. As an extra bonus for all their help, although I was in no doubt as to the value of the exhibition to them personally, I ensured that the costly return journey would not have to be made, by offering the exhibition unit to the Whiston Hospital to be used as a satellite dialysis unit. Geography never having been one of my top subjects, I realized later that perhaps my gesture was not quite such a valuable one since I had not appreciated the distance from London to Liverpool!

Three days before the exhibition was due to open I drove to London to encourage the men in their work. On arrival I found that David Cummings, the Director in charge of this particular operation, had been faithful to his word. The last blue shutter was being pinned in place, painted blue trellis broke the bareness of the walls, and the porch and steps that I had pleaded with him to have completed the picture of a warm and friendly building to welcome dialysis patients. One little feature had also been added for which I could not blame him. Following my instructions, on one side of the smart, wooden approach to the front door had been painted, larger than life, the logo of the BKPA – a kidney encircled by a laurel wreath. On the opposite side, where I expected to see our logo repeated, was an equally large sign depicting not only the Portakabin brand sign but also giving the telephone number where Portakabin could be contacted in York! It hurt me deeply to pick up the pot of blue paint standing nearby and, with great care, to paint out the offending advertisement. Quite apart from the fact that the sign was too large and inappropriate, I was very anxious that no one should have cause to imagine that perhaps the BKPA was open to persuasion by any commercial firm. In just the same way that the kidney machines in use at our holiday dialysis centre were chosen for no other reason than that they were in evidence in 82 per cent of renal units throughout the country, so Portakabin were chosen on merit.

The exhibition – if it could be called such, since it was not open to members of the public but only by appointment – was opened on the morning of 27 November by the Minister for Health. A number of journalists were present representing various medical publications and in my speech of thanks to the Minister I took the opportunity that presented itself to attack once more, kindly, the government – and National Health Service in particular – who continued to turn their backs on hundreds of their fellow citizens who were dying each year because no treatment could be offered them. It was my hope that if no further funds were to be injected into the Renal Replacement Programme, at least the funds already available might be put to better use and I urged those present to sing the praises of minimal care satellite units in general, and the one in which they were standing in particular. A number of the Regional Health Authority Chairmen had responded to the Department's circular and throughout the course of the six weeks came to visit me and discuss the various aspects of the scheme that I was suggesting. We had the largest home dialysis programme in Europe for no better reason than that it was the cheapest way of treating patients on dialysis, and I wanted to capitalize on that fact.

Today the cost of dialysing a patient in the hospital runs at between £12,000 and £14,000 a year per patient, by comparison with the home cost which can be as low as £8,000. Nevertheless, I knew that further cuts could be made if a number of patients were able to use the same facilities, thus reducing both capital expenditure and the revenue consequences. Home dialysis patients were scattered throughout the region served by their main dialysis unit and often the distance from the patient's home, where his machine was kept serviced and supplied, was as far as sixty miles from the base. These long distances had to be covered regularly, at great expense, by the technicians servicing the machines, the home dialysis administrator and social worker visiting the patient and his family, and the transport carrying the monthly supplies, making the end cost of the operation unnecessarily high. If my exhibition on the Foreign Office Green that winter had served to open the minds of the RHA Chairmen and a few renal consultants to the possibility of minimal care satellite units as an alternative to home dialysis, I would have been well pleased.

The excitement of those six weeks culminated in a fitting occasion. I received a call from 10 Downing Street just before the exhibition closed.

'This is Caroline Ryder, the Prime Minister's secretary,' the voice said. 'The Prime Minister noticed that you were not on the list of guests to be invited to a cocktail party at Number 10 to mark the International Year of the Disabled and has especially asked that you should receive an invitation. Can you come?'

I am sure that whatever I had planned to do that day would have been swiftly cancelled if at all possible, and I replied that I was free and would very much like to accept.

'Would it be all right, do you think, if I brought Timbo along with me?' I asked, and thankfully Caroline replied, 'Yes, I am sure that would be perfectly alright.'

Timbo, who had only recently been released from the Churchill Hospital after his third transplant operation, received the news with his usual nonchalance and told me he would let me know in a day or two whether he would be free! I have no doubt he was secretly as thrilled as I was but would certainly not have given me the satisfaction of knowing it.

Although I had been fortunate in meeting Mrs Thatcher on another occasion I had never before been inside the offical home of the Prime Minister. Timbo and I were greeted at the top of the long staircase by Mrs Thatcher, who enchanted me with her obvious delight at finding herself in occupation of one of the most historic houses in London.

'Have you ever been here before?' she asked, and on hearing that our visit was my first she continued confidentially, 'You simply must go into the small dining-room and have a look at some of the gorgeous pictures there, they are quite lovely.'

I told her later, in conversation, that I liked to think of her glancing out of her bathroom window each morning whilst cleaning her teeth, admiring the view of the blue and white BKPA minimal care dialysis satellite unit sitting on the Foreign Office Green!

'Oh, that's what it is. I often wondered,' was her retort.

Obviously a cocktail party at Number 10 Downing Street was not the place to discuss the shortcomings of the National Health Service and I told her how grateful I was to have had the use of her electricity supply and that I had proudly referred to the satellite unit as 'Number 10a'! Timbo, in the meantime, with long years of dietary restrictions placed behind him was interested in neither the grandeur of the occasion nor the fascinating political figures present but only in the plates of canapés that seemed miraculously to be constantly heading in his direction!

# 8

# Third Time Lucky

That summer, just before the date set for Timbo's third transplant, we broke with a tradition of many years. Turning our backs on the tiny rented fisherman's cottage on the beach at Kaminaki on the beautiful island of Corfu, where we usually went, we holidayed in the Seychelles. Trevor Huddleston, who at that time was Archbishop of the Indian Ocean and living in Mauritius, arranged for one of his regular trips to Mahe to coincide with ours. It would be foolish to pretend that I arrived on that beautiful island in a holiday mood since my concern for Timbo's deteriorating condition and fear of the outcome of the approaching transplant operation hung over me like a black cloud in an otherwise blue, blue sky. We stayed at the Fisherman's Cove Hotel, where a turquoise sea lapped idly on the silver sand, spread out like a mantle of the gods before our thatched log cabin. There were times, of course, when, cares and fears forgotten, I absolutely revelled in the beauty of the island, the heat of the sun, and the peace and quiet of such a paradise, but always my happiness was interrupted by the thought of what lay ahead for all of us.

One evening after dinner Trevor and I were sitting alone together and I had a chance to voice my fears.

'Why don't you write around to some of the Christian communities and ask them to pray for you?' Trevor asked.

'You are surely not being serious?' I replied. 'When half the population of thinking people are on their knees praying for world peace, how could I possibly write to ask people to pray for us? On the other hand,' I laughed, 'if you would like to write to them and ask them to pray for me, that would be quite another matter!'

I thought no more of our conversation but two or three weeks after my return home at the end of July I received the first letter from one of the communities that Trevor had mentioned. 'My good friend, Father Huddleston, has asked me...' it began, and it was followed shortly by five more letters written in the same vein from Abbots, Abbesses, and Mother Superiors, all showing their concern and promising to pray for a successful outcome to the operation.

Nigel had passed the various tests before the operation with flying colours and there was no going back. Always on the lookout for a 'good story', even when the story involved the misfortunes of my own son, I made quite sure the press knew of the latest development in the continuing saga of the family Ward! The week-end prior to the operation I appeared on Southern Television and a photo-call produced a lovely photograph of Timbo and Nigel looking gay and confident, as if a successful operation was behind them instead of yet to come. Timbo set the tone for that week-end and I remember it as being riotously funny as we basked in the warmth of his amazing humour, which never deserted him on such important occasions. He has never been a man for second gear. He was meant to enjoy each day as if it were his last, and has always known how to squeeze the last drop of value from every event and situation. He has always welcomed the challenge of a good fight even though he knew he was fighting for his life, but coping with a half-life or limbo world was beyond him. He was excited at the prospect of a new life again and, although well aware of all the pain that lay in store for him, he remained throughout those awful waiting days supremely confident and strong. I did my best to pick up his mood but despised myself for lack of faith and courage. When the day dawned I had plenty of both, no doubt given me by the many hundreds of people who were supporting me in prayer.

Timbo was admitted to the Churchill Hospital on Friday 29 August and Nigel joined him two days later. We drove together to Oxford, where I booked into my hotel, and we shared what I had begun to think might be our last meal together. I had been carried away on a tide of euphoria, joining excitedly in plans for a future for Timbo that we had begun to despair of his ever seeing. But now with the operation only hours away, doubts and fears rushed back and filled my troubled mind. Nigel, my precious companion of so many years, understood my anxious thoughts and started almost every fresh conversation with the words, 'I thought at the end of October we might...' or 'Why don't we for your birthday...' (which was in five weeks' time), or 'When Timbo's back on his feet again, it might make sense to...' in a vain attempt to dispel any thoughts that either of them had come to the end of the road. I responded bravely, and kept saying to myself under my breath, 'This time tomorrow it will all be over.' Little did I know!

The operation was planned to start at nine o'clock the next morning and I was at the hospital in good time to kiss them both and wish them luck. Becky, who loved us all, was there to share the waiting hours and we sat in the sun together on the lawn outside the small, single isolation ward to which Timbo would be returned when the operation was over. It was wonderful to have her with me, she had just returned from an amazing holiday cruising on a yacht around the Greek Islands, and listening to her cheerful narrative helped me keep my mind away from the scene inside the operating theatre.

Peter Morris, the transplanter, had told me that there was a 40/60 chance of Nigel's kidney working for Timbo and that if the kidney failed to function immediately he intended to remove it straightaway. His own feeling was that if the kidney did not work at once then it would not work at all, and he was not prepared to risk Timbo's life unnecessarily by fighting to keep the kidney from rejecting. This fair and straight pronouncement meant that time was not on his side. There was no question of saying to myself, 'Well, never mind. Perhaps it will work tomorrow, or if not tomorrow the next day, or the next week, or even next month.' Timbo's new kidney must be functioning before he left the operating theatre or he would never leave it with a new kidney at all.

They were both back in their beds by lunch-time and after paying a brief visit to Nigel in one part of the hospital I returned to the transplant block and, donning gloves, mask, and gown, I went into Timbo's room and sat by his bed. The kidney was working well – so far so good – but by six o'clock that evening he was complaining of extreme tenderness and immediately the signal 'rejection' went out. Peter Morris was sent for and after examining Timbo went into conference with his colleagues. I was absolutely petrified that they would remove the kidney, and equally positive that whatever the cause of the tenderness that Timbo felt it was not caused by rejection. In my endeavours to prevent them making a hasty decision I dropped Timbo right in it and told them of his low pain threshold. He was a new patient to them, and they had no previous experience of him so were, therefore, willing to accept my assurance and leave the decision-making for a few hours. Call it faith or what you will, but I absolutely knew for sure that the kidney would work for him and that he would be given another chance to lead a normal life. I did not just hope it, I knew it, and the knowledge came from deep inside me. I visited Nigel again and said goodnight and returned to my hotel to pray. Before I left the hospital Peter Morris told me that the results of Timbo's blood chemistry had not altered and that he could not account for what he called 'a sure outward sign of rejection'.

Much later that night, unable to sleep for fear that they might take him to theatre and remove the kidney before morning came, I telephoned Peter Morris at his home. It takes some courage for a mother with a reputation like mine to ring a transplant surgeon at his home number in the middle of the night, but such was my anxiety that I somehow found it. Peter gave me his assurance that he had no plans to get up in the middle of the night, get dressed, and return to the hospital to remove the precious kidney, and with that reassurance I finally fell asleep. On my way to the hospital the next morning I called into the studio of Radio Oxford at their invitation and was interviewed on their breakfast programme. I was in a buoyant mood on arriving at the surgical ward and found the transplant team standing at Nigel's bedside. Peter Morris looked across at me and smiling asked, 'Would you like to join my team as a soothsayer?'

Not for one moment would I deny the skills and expertise of Peter and his team, but I have not the slightest doubt in my own mind that Timbo's new kidney had been saved by the strength of prayer.

Nigel made a slow and steady recovery, returning home to me after only ten days in hospital, but it was to be several weeks before he rejoined me in our bedroom, choosing to sleep alone because of great discomfort and restless nights. Timbo was discharged two months after the operation and continued to keep cheerful and optimistic through weeks of set-backs and disappointment. Ten days after the operation, on the day of Nigel's release from hospital, they removed Timbo's catheter and within a matter of hours his bladder, unused to the flow of urine, sprung a leak so the catheter was reinserted. Two weeks later the same thing happened again. I could have wept and probably did, unbeknown to him, but I remember him saying, 'Don't worry, Mum. After all, what's a few extra weeks in hospital when I have the whole of my life ahead of me?'

I visited him daily, filling the long driving hours by dictating letters on my tape-machine in reply to ones I had read at traffic-lights and other traffic hold-ups. Every day I called at a small, family grocer's in Headington, where they sold Timbo's favourite ham and where the shopkeeper and his wife came to eagerly await news of Timbo's progress. His walls were festooned with cards from well-wishers, relatives, friends, and complete strangers. When we finally took them down the day he left the hospital I counted over 300. I used the Churchill Hospital as a venue for meeting journalists, and television and radio researchers, and we would sit outside his isolation ward on the grass discussing in detail the script or story. One day it was all over. I wish I could have thought that I had made many friends whilst I was there throughout the long nine weeks of his stay, but apart from one charming kitchen cleaner and a junior nurse personal contact with any of the nursing staff somehow escaped me. It had been a lonely, trying time and we were both glad when it was all over.

Nineteen-eighty-one was an uneventful year for the BKPA, which continued to expand both in terms of fund raising and the demands made upon its resources. I was invited to address the All-Party Disablement Group at Westminster and the story I had to tell so horrified my listeners that the following Monday they sent a deputation round to the Secretary of State for Health and Social Services demanding more facilities for kidney patients. How simple it would all have been if awareness were all that was needed to ensure an end to the unnecessary suffering and deaths of so many people, but it seemed that although the government of the day – any government – was always able to find extra funds to enable a dramatic dash to be made to the rescue of the victims of flood, hurricanes, and earthquakes in other countries, it was quite unable to find the extra money needed annually to come to the rescue of its own countrymen.

I was both disappointed and angry in turns by the failure of the government's kidney donor card scheme and their persistent rejection of the alternative 'opting out' scheme. This was something Tam Dalyell, the Labour MP for Midlothian, had introduced in a Private Member's Bill in the mid-seventies, calling for legislation to allow donor kidneys to be taken from cadavers unless the patient, in his lifetime, had recorded his dissent. The Bill, which was introduced on a number of occasions, never got beyond the first reading and by 1981 Tam Dalyell was sadly more concerned with the situation in Northern Ireland than he was with the

unnecessary deaths of the patients suffering from renal
failure. I had been energetically supporting 'opting out'
legislation, which had already been successfully introduced in
a number of Western European countries, since I felt
convinced that the kidney donor card would never become a
satisfactory means of making donor kidneys available for
transplantation. A Gallop survey which I had commissioned
at about that time showed that whilst 69 per cent of the adult
population were willing for their kidneys to be used after
death for transplant purposes, only 10 per cent of those
people actually carried a donor card. Given that kidney
donor cards had been on the market, albeit not readily
available, for the past ten years, I thought the time had come
reluctantly to accept the failure of the scheme.

I was obviously intrigued to know why the Private
Member's Bill was constantly thrown out by the House of
Commons and I learned that one good reason was the
opposition to the Bill by a certain MP representing the Jewish
community. I sought an interview with the Chief Rabbi, Dr
Jakobovits, who readily agreed to meet me in one of the small
meeting-rooms at the House of Commons. I found him a
fascinating man of quiet strength who genuinely believed that
'opting out' legislation would interfere with the rights of the
individual.

'But don't you understand,' I said, 'that the present system
ensures interference with the rights of the individual, since
though you might have expressed your wish for your kidneys
to be used after your death, your nearest and dearest can
ignore your wishes and refuse to allow your kidneys to be
removed.'

I knew, of course, that there was a very healthy transplant
programme being carried out in Israel but I found it difficult
to accept his reluctance to support a Bill that appeared to me
to be the answer to such tragic, wicked waste of life. I was
unable to convince him, but before we parted he said, 'I am
really sorry that I am not able to help you in the way that you
would like but is there any other way in which I can help you?'

My response was immediate. 'Oh, Dr Jakobovits, you are kind. You are the head of a rich and powerful community. Do you think you could perhaps write round to some of the Chairmen of such companies as Tesco and Marks and Spencer and tell them how much I need their help?'

He promised he would get in touch with them and as we ascended in the lift together I told him that some years before I had been much impressed by a speech that his predecessor had made at the Institute of Directors' annual conference at the Albert Hall. Lifting his hands to his generous girth, he smiled, and said, 'Oh no, not my predecessor. I am afraid that was me!'

He was as good as his word and a few days after our meeting I received a letter from his assistant, Moshi Davies, letting me know that the Chief Rabbi had written to the Chairmen of some of the larger companies seeking help on my behalf.

On the home front it was a year of 'off with the old and on with the new', and much personal grief and anguish found its way into my home that year. Susie, who had been called to the Bar some years before but had never practised, had decided to become articled to a solicitor as her marriage was on the rocks. She had been working as an international maritime lawyer with a P&I club before her marriage, but had moved to Norfolk to be with her husband David. When they finally parted she was anxious to come and live near me since she knew I would welcome the children and help if I could. With two small children and little money it was very difficult for her to manage life without my help for a period, and I was only too pleased to have Katherine and Charles to stay on many occasions throughout her settling-down period. After much hardship and anxiety she found a keeper's cottage to rent seven miles from my own home and the same distance from Winchester, where she began her articles all over again.

Timbo, who had always threatened once he was free of the

machine to go back to Australia and make his life there, had been given the all-clear by Peter Morris and on 30 September we drove him to Gatwick Airport with enough luggage to last him a lifetime. He had had to get professional help with the filling-in of his emigration papers, which clearly showed that the Australian authorities were anxious to welcome to their shores only fit and healthy emigrants! Someone who loved him must have been prepared to perjure themselves on his behalf in the signing of the forms and I was grateful to them, really, because I had meant it when I said to him, 'I would not mind if I never saw you again so long as I can be sure you are happy.'

We discussed the possibility of his death in Australia and I told him that if he died out there I would like to hold a thanksgiving service for him at St Peter's, Eaton Square. His reaction was positive. 'You must do what you like but don't do it for my sake! The idea of a whole lot of people coming together saying how wonderful I was when they could hardly say anything else seems stupid, and anyway how would you feel if nobody turned up?'

He didn't like the idea, though, of his body being left to rest in Australia. I told him that his father, with whom I had also, of course, discussed the fearful possibility, had no intention of wasting money bringing home a body for cremation in England.

'I wouldn't have thought,' he said, 'that you would like to think of me so far away.'

He was right, I certainly would not and planned that somehow, if that time came, I would get his body back to England.

To break the seriousness of the conversation he finished up on a typically macabre note: 'And when I am cremated I would either like my ashes scattered from the top of the Post Office Tower or else you could divide them equally into five and send them to my special friends in a little jar marked "T"!'

Having lived over the past ten years immersed in the problems of other dialysis and transplant patients, and knowing full well the disasters that can strike when least expected, it was hard for me to share in his excited mood on the drive to Gatwick Airport. The air hostess at the check-in point viewed his five large suitcases with respect, thinking no doubt he was heir to a small fortune – and who was about to see some of it handed over! The excess baggage came to over £60, so we removed it from the scales and, with my two shy companions standing behind me engaged in earnest conversation, I watched the scales and waited for the passengers with hand-luggage or only one suitcase well below the limit. With only two passengers left to check in we finally got all his baggage distributed at no extra cost to ourselves. At last he was off. I hugged him and smiled, wished him luck, and kept my tears for the journey home.

Only two weeks later we said goodbye to Becky at the same airport and on this occasion, because we were girls together, the tears flowed without repression. Becky had apparently fallen in love with a charming Texan who worked as a mud engineer on an oil rig off Jakarta. She was determined to fly to Singapore and stay for a few months, with a view to marriage, and whilst not wanting to alienate her from us forever, I think she was left in no doubt as to how unsuitable we felt her choice to be. We knew she was making a great mistake and were fearful for her own happiness. Of course I was going to miss her terribly, and with Timbo gone it was difficult to lose her so quickly, but had she been going for the right reasons I would have more readily accepted her departure. I had given them each, as a small leaving present, a Philips cassette recorder together with a good supply of tapes and so although I was in danger of forgetting the size and shape of their handwriting I would never forget the sound of their much-loved voices. We talked to each other on tape each week and as it is much easier to talk than to write I was kept up to date with their thoughts and activities.

Such was my love for Timbo that I had really meant it when I said that if the price I would have to pay for his happiness was never to see him again, then it would be a small price indeed. He had suffered so much for so long that all I wanted for him was the chance to lead a proper life, free of pain and fear, able to join in the young fun of his friends, get his head down to some worthwhile work, and hopefully one day get married to a lovely girl who would care for him and love him as I did. If he felt he had to travel to the other side of the world to achieve this, then so be it.

His plan was to stay a few weeks with Clive and Vicky whilst he found himself a job and could become independent of them. Nigel had given him a reasonable sum of money to last him six weeks or so, in the hope that he would land himself a job and be earning his own living before the money ran out. He had been led to believe that gold lay on the pavement ready to be picked up by anyone who had the will and energy to stoop, but it seemed that that was not the case. He told us in his second tape that he had so far drawn a blank on job hunting. With Christmas approaching, he said, all the university and college students were picking up the odd jobs, and being English and unknown he was never the one chosen. We had hoped that he would have made contact with some of the many names and addresses we had given him, and certainly his godmother had come up with a most impressive list of influential people who we were sure could have helped him. For some reason, which we never discovered, he made contact with none of the people whose addresses he had with him and the only money he ever earned whilst he was there was for selling Biros door-to-door for one week.

Much to our disappointment Becky had suddenly decided to bring the proposed date of her marriage to Gary forward by several months, to 1 December. A date had been fixed in March the following year, and Nigel and I would have flown out to Singapore for the wedding. It was many weeks ahead and I felt sure that common sense would prevail and Becky would realize that she was making a grave mistake and would return home before it was too late. She had, however, made all plans for her wedding on the new date with her future mother-in-law and as we were being told, rather than asked, and as the date she had chosen was only a matter of days ahead and Nigel's diary during that particular time was even fuller than mine, we told her that we couldn't go. I was absolutely devastated. The thought of Becky being married without me, no matter how unsuitable the man she had chosen, was beyond belief. My princess, as I had often called her, was going to spend the most important day of her life without her loving Mama, with whom she had so often planned an imaginary wedding. As one friend after another had answered the call of marriage she was always full of plans for her own. At last her turn had come and she had chosen to do it all without me and my heart was heavy.

Nigel was furious, but I was pleased, that Timbo had used his Diner's card to book a seat to Singapore and was there on her great day to give her away. I asked our local vicar, in whose church we had always dreamed her wedding would take place, if we could go in the morning and spend a little time there together on our own. We arrived at the church in separate cars, as I was on my way to Liverpool to take part in a seminar, at precisely the same time as she would be arriving at the church in Singapore, taking into account the seven hours' difference between the two countries. We sat together in the small, empty church, holding hands and praying for her happiness and the success of her marriage. Although I had no idea what her dress looked like, nor could I picture the church or the face of the man who was marrying her, or those surrounding her, at least I could picture the faces of her and Timbo and Gary, my new son-in-law. Some weeks later, after Christmas, the photographs of her great day arrived but I found it hard to look at them and not feel a little sad and bitter.

Christmas that year was remarkable only for the way it differed from Christmases before. For the first time Timbo and Becky were not with us and we were forcibly reminded of the unhappiness in Susie's life by the removal of the grandchildren on Boxing Day by their father David; the agony of sharing had begun. David had recently come back to live in London after two years working in Tokyo for his company. When Katherine heard that her father was returning home she said to me wistfully one day, 'Oh Granny, wouldn't it be wonderful if Daddy could come and live in the cottage next door?' She obviously understood that there was no question of Daddy coming to live with them again, but having him close would have been nice.

Then we heard that Timbo had been involved in a road accident. He was bicycling through the city of Melbourne when a child suddenly appeared from behind a bus. He swerved to avoid it, fell off his bicycle, and the pedal dug deeply into the side of his leg. Because his tissues were so frail the wound refused to heal and it was decided that a skin-graft was needed. He was admitted to Prince Henry's Hospital for surgery and a section of skin was taken from his upper thigh and stitched over the offending hole in his calf. Because of the steroids that he was taking to prevent rejection of Nigel's kidney the graft did not take properly, and he was told that it would be several weeks before he could put his foot to the ground. The opportunity for job hunting ended overnight so, with his money running out and no prospect of work in the future, there was no alternative but for him to ask us to get him home. It must have been a bitter blow for him and caused me great sadness since I knew how much he had set his heart on making a life for himself in Australia and how very much he wanted to shake free from the past. It was particularly hard on him that his hopes were shattered, not by a failed transplant, but an ordinary accident that could have happened to anyone. As he said on the telephone, 'I wouldn't have minded so much if I had been driving a lime green Porsche – but a bicycle!'

Timbo home again, jobless and destitute, I was faced once more with the pressing problem of how best to help him. One of his many friends came to his rescue with an offer of accommodation and I rang around mine to try to get him work. It was a difficult, disillusioning time for him, urged on as he was by the thought that his new kidney would not last him forever and by his anxiety to make the most of his freedom from the machine. After his return from Australia he was unemployed for six months and I seemed powerless to help him. Like hundreds of other kidney patients throughout the country he sat in his room writing letters in reply to newspaper advertisements and went for endless interviews, and the response was the same: 'I am very sorry but, of course, with your medical condition it would not be possible for us to offer you the job.' I had urged him not to disclose the fact that he was a transplant patient but I realized that I was being unrealistic. As he pointed out to me, he frequently had to drive to Oxford to clinic and sooner or later his new employers would have discovered his condition. He had his longed-for freedom but life passed him by, and with no skills to offer and in poor health he was heading for the scrap-heap at the age of twenty-nine.

With those heartaches to cope with I was grateful to have the needs and problems of kidney patients and their families to take my mind off the needs and problems of my own.

I had been fortunate in early 1980 to interest the BBC in our first holiday dialysis centre and a camera crew had come down and taken a charming film of the children from Booth Hall renal unit in Manchester, who were dialysing with us on holiday at the time. They were interviewed both on dialysis and having fun in the holiday village, and the result was a tear-jerking ten-minute insight into the lives of these children and how they coped.

The children who took part in the film, Tracy, Allison, Gillian, and Sharon were all lovely girls at whom fate had struck a cruel blow, and all were in need of dialysis. Allison, the baby of the quartet at eleven, seemed by far the fittest and liveliest of the group. The first heat of the Donkey Derby showed Sharon and Tracy completing for last place, with Tracy's donkey, having given up altogether standing lazily cropping the grass. The second heat showed Allison's donkey coming up from behind and, much to the delight of the crowd, winning by a good head. It was a lovely, happy film showing how things can be despite the need for treatment on a kidney machine and consequently my sadness was very real when I learned that three weeks after the children had returned home to Manchester Allison had died after transplantation.

Later that year we went up to Manchester and fêted the stars of our first real fund-raising film. Gavin, Allison's twin brother, came to join in the fun, which was shared by some of the other young patients from the Manchester children's unit. We presented the children with travelling clocks and after showing the film I sought our Mrs Dawson, Allison's mother. 'I think you are very specal to come today and I hope that seeing the film didn't hurt you too much.'

'Oh no, Mrs Ward,' she replied. 'You don't understand. You see now we no longer think of Allison with tubes and pipes and things, we only think of her winning the Donkey Derby.'

I realized then that I was doing more than giving a much-needed break to dialysis patients and their partners. I was helping to wipe out pictures of fear and pain and replacing them with memories of joy and happiness.

I had had the film with me during my exhibition on the Foreign Office Green and I had the inspired thought to invite Prince Philip's equerry, Major John Cargin, to come and see the film. I was plucking up the courage to invite Prince Philip to visit my holiday dialysis centre and, when I did, John Cargin would at least know how to advise him.

# 9

# From Trinkets to Treasure

The official visit by Prince Philip to my holiday dialysis centre at Earnley, near Bracklesham Bay, was one of several exciting events that occupied some of my time during 1982. I had been very disappointed when Prince Philip had to cancel his visit to my holiday dialysis centre, which had been planned for 29 July, the previous year. Prince Charles had chosen that date to marry the beautiful Lady Diana Spencer. Buckingham Palace had assured me that another date would be found the following year and true to their word, at the begining of 1982 I received news from Prince Philip's equerry that a new date had been fixed for the visit – 29 July again.

With much excitement, and the help of Laurence Scragg, I set about making arrangements well in advance to welcome him. The plan was that Prince Philip would arrive by helicopter on the recreation area in the middle of the holiday village adjoining our holiday dialysis centre. Gerald West-minster had paid us a visit the previous summer, also arriving by helicopter, so I knew that the site chosen was both safe and suitable. I received a call from Buckingham Palace, anxious to arrange a date when I could meet Prince Philip's pilot together with the senior police officer in charge of the security for the royal visit. Up until then I had hardly dared to believe that it was really happening – that Prince Philip, one of the best loved and most sought after members of the Royal family, was actually making time in his busy life to pay an official visit to my holiday dialysis centre on the West Sussex coast and show us that he cared, too.

I have often been amazed by my own daring and audacity, although only in retrospect, and this was such an occasion. I had made a definite plan to invite Prince Philip officially to open the first holiday dialysis centre of its kind in the country and, truthfully, I had schemed to that end so that at the time it seemed to me quite natural that my invitation to Prince Philip should have been accepted, but looking back on that day I can still ask in wonderment, 'Did it really happen to me?' I think now, if I had realized the organization required and understood the true implications of the need for top security, I might well have been daunted and hesitant in making such a request but somehow, miraculously, everything fell into place and with the amazing cooperation of Ken Newington and the staff at the holiday village, the police, and the local garrison, the day went off without a hitch and hopefully was enjoyed by one and all.

Without a doubt this was to be the most exciting day in the short history of the BKPA and I was determined that all who had given me their much-needed support over the years would be there to share in my triumph. I invited representatives from BKPA branches, Guides, Brownies, WIs, and many other ardent supporters, together with patients and their relatives and, of course, my family and friends. Mary Graves, whose two family trusts had made possible the financing of the holiday centre, was also there with her husband Desmond to be presented when the time came.

The order of the day began with the arrival of Prince Philip by helicopter at 2.30 p.m. when he was received by myself, and Nigel and Timbo were then presented to him. We walked from the helicopter past a mass of shouting, cheering, flag-waving holiday-makers until we arrived at the top of the wide, paved path leading down to the entrance to the centre. At either side of the path hundreds of patients, relatives, and fund raisers jostled for better positions or a chance to talk to Prince Philip as he moved from side to side. Cameras clicked, voices were raised in laughter, faces wreathed in happy smiles, and the honour was mine to escort this very special man to view the fruits of my labours and the realization of a dream; it was heady stuff. Prince Philip visited both treatment rooms, where I presented the staff to him and he had a chance to talk to the patients who were dialysing. He was particularly impressed by the large and fearsome-looking needles that they have inserted into their arms each session, and paid a special interest in the portable kidney machine we had on display for him. It meant a lot to me to know that I was introducing him to something new, another side of life which he had not seen before, since it was the first visit that he had ever made to a dialysis centre and the first time he had ever seen a person on a kidney machine. I made a short speech of welcome and thanks and Prince Philip replied after unveiling the plaque which commemorated his visit. He stayed for tea and chatted informally over cucumber sandwiches, showing a friendly interest in all I had to tell him. At four o'clock his car arrived and the send off he received can have left him with little doubt as to the happiness his visit had spread amongst us all.

As the fund grew and my efforts on behalf of kidney patients became known throughout the renal world, I was approached on an increasing number of occasions not only by patients themselves, desperate for financial help, but also by renal consultants. By the beginning of 1981 we had come to the rescue, in a practical way, of a number of schemes and programmes that would have foundered without financial help.

The previous year I had visited the Yorkhill Hospital, Glasgow, a large children's hospital which housed the only paediatric renal unit in the whole of Scotland. Children from all over the country in need of dialysis and transplantation homed in on this small life-saving centre, which was thoroughly inadequate for their needs. I had learnt on a previous visit that annually around a dozen children died in Scotland of end-stage renal failure because treatment could not be offered them in their country.

The titular head of the Yorkhill Hospital renal unit was Professor Gavin Arneil but the doctor in charge of the day to day running of the unit was a charming, compassionate, lovely lady called Anna Murphy and she and I had become firm friends. I was horrified at the cramped conditions under which she had to work and enthusiastically absorbed her plans for a new unit. Anna and Gavin had approached the Greater Glasgow Health Board on many occasions, only to be told that there was no available funding to meet their demands. I decided, and fortunately my Council approved my decision, that the building of a new paediatric renal unit, to be sited in Glasgow, to meet the needs of the children of Scotland would not only be expedient from the medical viewpoint but would also serve to establish the fact that a charity that chanced to have its headquarters in the South of England was nevertheless concerned for the welfare of the patients in the North.

In anticipation of a cooperative response from the Health Board working plans had been drawn up and a site chosen for the erection of the new building. I proposed a joint venture and offered to pay for the building if the Greater Glasgow Health Board would cover the revenue consequences. Meetings had been held on a number of occasions in the presence of Sir Simpson Stevenson, the Chairman of the Board, and on each occasion I had had my offer turned down.

'It's all very well for you to offer to pay for the building, Mrs Ward, but where are we to find the money for the running of the new unit? As soon as we have a large children's unit here in Glasgow we will get more and more patients referred.'

'But Sir Simpson,' I replied, 'Surely you are not telling me that you are prepared to sit there and acknowledge the fact that a number of your own small countrymen are sentenced to death each year because you are not prepared to allocate the necessary funds to save their lives. Can there be anything more important?'

After the last such interchange I had stormed out of the boardroom and within days was sitting in the office of the Scottish Minister for Health, Russell Fairgrieve, in Whitehall begging him to intervene. He was a true Scot and could not believe that anyone could turn down an offer of financial help to the tune of over £300,000, and I think was more impressed by that thought than that nearly forty children had died in Scotland untreated over the past three years. He promised his help and he kept his promise.

At the beginning of 1982 I received a friendly letter from Sir Simpson letting me know that the Health Board felt they were now in a position to cover the revenue consequences of the new unit and inviting me back to Glasgow to discuss my offer. Eighteen months before I had been talking about covering the cost of a brick-built renal unit costing in the region of a quarter of a million pounds. By the time my offer had been accepted the cost of the same building had escalated to well over £300,000 and the completion date was nearly two years away. In that time more little crosses would have gone up in graveyards throughout Scotland and I was not prepared to allow this to happen. I withdrew my offer of covering the cost of a brick-built renal unit and replaced it by offering to cover the cost in full of a modular building which, from my own experience with Portakabin, could be erected and ready for use four months after site clearance. They were not too happy about the change of plan but I think that they had all suffered enough from the media exposure to be prepared once more to turn down my offer of help. On my return to the office I contacted David Cummings of Portakabin and he and a colleague flew the next day to Glasgow for discussions with Gavin Arneil and Anna Murphy.

I had wanted so much for the building to be fully operational to commemorate the International Year of the

Child (1982) but as it was, despite the speed with which Portakabin got the talks under way, the discussions seemed endless to me and the site clearing, once begun, took many months. The Princess of Wales accepted my invitation to open the new unit to coincide with the centenary of Yorkhill Hospital on 17 February 1983. Dick White, the paediatric nephrologist on my Council, flew up to Glasgow to share in that great occasion and assured me that it was the finest paediatric renal unit in the country, where all aspects of the treatment of renal disease, except transplantation, were taken care of under one roof. Anna Murphy was overjoyed and the £310,000, the biggest single sum that the BKPA had paid out, was, I felt, truly well spent.

I had heard, like everyone else, of the amazing sums of money raised by the BBC's 'Blue Peter' appeals and I was determined that one day I should land this one myself. I knew that with the correct approach our story was a natural for the Blue Peter audience. The plight of children of their own age destined to live their lives attached to a kidney machine three times a week, having to turn their backs on much of the fun enjoyed by their friends, unable to indulge in sweet eating or Coke drinking, denied the freedom of visiting friends and relations, was something with which they could identify. Three years before I had been given a slot on 'The Week's Good Cause'. I had written the text myself and, much against the advice of the BBC, I personally made the appeal. Most of the BBC appeals were made by people with well-known names, famous actors and film stars, MPs and sportsmen, all good people putting their name to a worthy cause. But mine was an unknown name and the BBC was afraid of a failure. I was convinced that what was important was not that I should be a famous person with a well-known voice, but that I should be speaking from the heart about a problem that I understood because I had experienced it personally. Fortunately my instinct was right. The appeal raised more money than any other single appeal bar one since the first was made in 1937, so I had been shown the strength of feeling, and had experienced the tide of sympathy, that was felt by the British public towards patients on dialysis.

It followed that I found it difficult to understand why such an obvious choice as the BKPA could be ignored year after year by the BBC as a candidate for 'Blue Peter'! Every new emotive story concerning the plight of dialysis children found its way to the desk of the programme's producer, Biddy Baxter. I personally took a copy of our short fund-raising film showing the Manchester children having fun at our holiday dialysis centre and beseeched her secretary to ensure that Biddy Baxter saw the film herself. A week later I rang her office: 'Has she seen the film yet?' I asked.

'No,' replied her secretary, 'I'm afraid Miss Baxter is very busy planning the next appeal.'

My heart sank, it seemed the chance had passed me by once more.

Meanwhile, Laurence had arranged a fund-raising tour of army units in Germany and had been to a great deal of trouble in planning it. He had written to the wives of Generals, Brigadiers, and Division Commanders of the Rhine, and had made all travel arrangements including the reservation of hotel accommodation in every town we planned to visit. He had been working on what we both saw as an important fund raising trip for several months, so it was not hard for me to anticipate the utter disbelief with which he greeted the news that I had been summoned to the Blue Peter office on 19 October, the very day of our departure to Hamburg! The call had come the previous Thursday afternoon.

'Biddy Baxter would like to see you at her office at 11.30 next Tuesday to discuss the possibility of your charity benefiting from the next Blue Peter Appeal. She would like you to bring with you to the meeting details of the items you require together with appropriate costings.'

The chance of an appeal on the Blue Peter programme was so sought after by the heads of charities throughout the country that it was obviously not thought necessary to give fair warning to the charity under consideration. It was naturally expected that I would down tools, cancel all plans and other arrangements, and make myself immediately available when the call came, and so, of course, I did. I put down the phone shaking with excitement, but my first thought was for poor Laurence. After the initial reaction of fury followed by indignation, protest, and bitter disappointment, common sense prevailed and he realized that whilst we could not assume the appeal would be ours we could not possibly turn our backs on the chance of landing it.

My next thought was what to appeal for, since I knew that vast sums of money were raised by the Appeal each year and I also realized how important it was to be able to project the need in an interesting and attractive way to the young viewers. We had so many needs, plans, and hopes for the future, but not all of them were suitable for a continuous television programme. I thought of the Hospital for Sick Children, Great Ormond Street, and my concern that many of the young patients attending the renal clinic there would one day have to face the need for dialysis, and that when that day came they would always be shipped off to a paediatric renal unit in another part of London because there were no dialysis facilities for them at Great Ormond Street. I had for a long time wanted to be in a position to provide dialysis facilities for the hospital, but I knew that a large sum of money was required and so I had had to shelve that particular plan for the future.

I rang Professor Martin Barratt, the senior consultant in charge of the renal clinic at Great Ormond Street. 'Martin,' I said, 'you'll hardly believe this but I think there's a chance that I might get the Blue Peter Appeal and you might get your dialysis facilities at last. Biddy Baxter needs a project, a target, and costings by Tuesday. Can you do it?'

'But Liz,' came the reply, 'it is already Thursday afternoon and there is a week-end between now and next Tuesday. How can I possibly get everything put together by then? I need the permission of the Governor, the approval of the Administrator, plans drawn up by an architect, we'll need costings and, of course, from somewhere we will have to find the revenue consequences of running this new ward.'

'Oh Martin, please, please,' I begged. 'I know you can do this and you know it is what we both want so much. Please will you try?'

'I'll do my best,' he said, and hung up.

I cannot imagine what went on at his end but he moved with amazing speed, whipping up such enthusiasm and cooperation that by Monday afternoon he was in a position to ring me and tell me that the rough drawings and costings were being sent by Pony Express to arrive at the BBC studios at Shepherd's Bush the following morning to coincide with my meeting with Biddy Baxter. True to his word, when Laurence and I arrived I was handed a large buff-coloured envelope by the hall porter and had time to look through the contents briefly before the meeting.

There was so much at stake that I found the meeting nerve-racking and difficult, but it seemed that we had passed the test despite one awkward moment when Biddy Baxter, used to dealing with such giants as Oxfam, the Spastics Society and the Royal National Lifeboat Institution, asked, 'Are the other executives of the same calibre as yourselves?'

'Apart from the three clerical staff,' I replied, 'you are looking at the whole of the BKPA; there is only Laurence and me.'

We left with the feeling that the appeal would be ours although it was early days to celebrate. That meeting with Biddy Baxter on 19 October was to be the first of many and by early November I knew for sure that the 1982 Blue Peter Appeal would be launched on 15 November. The Appeal was to be in the form of a treasure hunt, and viewers were to be asked to send in such items as lead soldiers, broken watches, unwanted rings and costume jewellery, and the money raised was for the refurbishing and equipping of an acute renal care ward at the Hospital for Sick Children, Great Ormond Street.

I had two weeks in which to locate the premises for the appeal, and employ a manager and staff to open and sort the parcels, before the first mail-bags were expected to arrive. I found a large, empty warehouse on a trading estate only three miles from my office which I was able to rent for a three-month period, by which time we all expected the parcels would have been opened and the contents sorted and sold. In fact it was to be fifteen months before the last parcel was opened on 31 March 1984! During that time we received over 9,000 mail-bags and more than 300 tons of parcels whose contents were finally sold for the staggering sum of over two and a half million pounds.

The scale of the operation was so vast as to be almost unbelievable. Well before the three-month lease was up on the first building I was looking for other even larger premises. Fortunately for me the adjoining warehouse was available on a twenty-five year lease and using a great deal of persuasion I finally got the landlord to agree to let it to me for a twelve-month period. I extended the lease on the original premises for a further six months anticipating that by that time we would have cleared one building and be able to operate only from the other. The BBC, obviously having no conception of the strength of the response to their appeal, told us that we must be sure to open the mail-bags in order of delivery! We dutifully marked out in chalk on the warehouse floor six squares marked 'Monday' to 'Saturday' but by the end of November Monday's mail had spread into Wednesday and Wednesday's into Saturday's, and back again, and by Christmas the mail-bags reached the ceiling of the warehouse thirty deep. A staff of twenty-four working from nine to five made little impression on the ever-increasing pile of mail-bags.

By the beginning of the New Year Roadline, the national delivery service, had begun their free deliveries. The pantechnicon arrived daily from Southampton (the nearest Roadline depot to Bordon) bringing parcels sent in by viewers from all over the country. The men in the warehouse

left their parcel-opening to unload and stack the packages,
and then returned to the fascinating task of sorting the
articles into categories: the gold from the rolled gold; the
silver from the plate; the beads from the gems. I had never
seen anything like it, it was indeed a treasure hunt second to
none and the warehouse looked like the inside of Aladdin's
cave. The army came to our rescue with packing-cases and by
the end of January we were ready for our first dealers' sale.

I had borrowed the services of an excellent auctioneer from
Spink, the art dealers in London, who came down to the
trading estate regularly every alternate Friday to preside over
what must have been 'the sales of the century'. Tom Ayres, a
local jeweller friend of mine, gave up his time voluntarily
every week to advise us on the value of the items that we had
been given. Two of the girls working for me came with a
certain knowledge of the jewellery and silver trade, but long
before the last sale was held they had become veritable
experts.

We lost count of the number of gold wedding-rings at
20,000, and of watches after we'd counted over 35,000, but I
do remember that we had 11,321 cameras sent in to us, several
of them worth many hundred pounds. I threw myself with
vigour into the organization of one of the most exciting
events in my life, but somehow managed to prevent myself
being completely swamped by the appeal and continued to
run my office as before.

The overwhelming generosity of the viewers, together with
my determination to squeeze the last drop of value from every
parcel sent us, ensured that Martin Barratt got the dialysis
facilities he so badly needed at Great Ormond Street in
addition to a three-year commitment from the BKPA for
£30,000 annually in revenue consequences. The success of the
appeal enabled us to donate a piece of vital and expensive
equipment to all the paediatric renal units throughout the
country and to make a grant of £1,000 annually for five years
to help cover the immediate needs of their young patients.
When all was paid for and all donations made there was still

over £2 million undistributed, so with the approval of the BBC and the Charity Commissioners I set up a special Children's Trust within the framework of the BKPA, which, with the clever management of Cazenove, my stockbrokers, would make available around a quarter of a million pounds annually to well and truly cover the needs of young renal patients throughout the country.

At the same time that I was negotiating for the Blue Peter Appeal I was involved with the launching of the BKPA Investment Trust. The previous year I had read in the *Financial Times* of the success of the Child Health Research Investment Trust and I could see an investment trust as yet another way of not only raising more funds for the association, but of involving people of substance with the plight of the patients. Hitherto, apart from the odd Chairman and Trust, most of the money raised had come from those people who could ill-afford to part with their donations but were sufficiently compassionate and understanding to want to help. I had not, on the whole, attracted support from those people who, having had their nests feathered for them, could well afford to feather other people's. An investment trust seemed a wonderful opportunity to broaden my base even more and I grasped it with both hands. I had read that Cazenove, the leading City stockbrokers, were the brains behind the investment trust so I decided to make contact with the senior partner and try my luck. I rang the number and got through to the switchboard operator. Fearing that the senior partner might well be one of those with a protective barrier surrounding him I said, 'I wonder if you could put me through to your senior partner. It's so silly of me, I know his name so well. It's been on the tip of my tongue all morning but it has absolutely flown my mind.'

'Yes, certainly,' she replied, much to my surprise. 'The name is Mr John Kemp-Welsh; I am putting you through now.'

He sounded a little surprised as I tumbled into my spiel but he also sounded warm and friendly, if firm. 'I'm very sorry,

Mrs Ward,' he said, 'there is not the slightest chance of us setting up another investment trust for your charity as we've already got all the support we could expect from our own clients and to form another investment trust would be fishing in the same pool.'

Something in the tone of his voice gave me inspiration to reply, 'All I ask is that you should say "no" to my face. Please, Mr Kemp-Welsh, that cannot be too much to ask, can it?'

He laughed, perhaps he was intrigued, and made a date for me to meet him at his office the following week.

I returned from London that day with a promise that if I could persuade people to pledge their support for the issue with money, then Cazenove would arrange the issue and assemble the necessary professional advisers. With the support of a world-famous, well-established firm behind me I doubted that I would find it too difficult to interest potential investors. In fact it did not prove difficult to rally the support that I needed, the difficulties lay with the Inland Revenue who were not prepared to accept the setting up of the Trust in its proposed form. We had been so near the launching date that I had been devastated at the latest turn of events and immediately rang my friend, Gerry Vaughan, the Minister for Health and asked him to write to the Chairman of the Inland Revenue Board explaining the importance of the work of the BKPA in the hope of influencing their decision. Gerry's reaction was so positive and helpful that it encouraged me to write to the Prime Minister asking her for her intervention on my behalf. I had forgotten that she had been a tax lawyer, or perhaps I would not have written, but she replied at length explaining why the present scheme would not be acceptable to the Inland Revenue. She finished her letter by saying that she knew I would be disappointed by her reply and hoped most sincerely that I would find an alternative acceptable form so that the Investment Trust could be launched. My wonderful City friends put their heads together and set about adapting the original scheme to a form acceptable to the Inland Revenue, and on 22 November the BKPA Investment

Trust Plc was launched. As further evidence of the support that I was receiving from all who I came into contact with, all the individuals, companies, and firms involved in the launching of the Investment Trust gave their services without charge.

Earlier in 1982 I had succumbed to the pressure of the kidney patients who had successfully and happily holidayed at Sussex Beach for two years and were now calling for the sun. 'Oh please, Mrs Ward, couldn't you open a holiday dialysis centre for us where it is warm?' was the cry. France seemed to be the most popular country of their choice so in the autumn of that year I travelled down by car with Laurence Scragg to try to find a suitable location. I had an open mind on whether to rent, or buy, or find a plot of land on which to put a Portakabin. I was looking for a seaside resort, not too fashionable, with plenty of entertainment, a good, safe beach, and easily accessible by road, air, and rail. It took me a week to find it, but when we drove into La Grande Motte one late afternoon I knew that my search was at an end.

Two trips later I found the perfect place; a beautiful third-floor apartment overlooking the marina on one side and the sea on the other, where the patients could sit during dialysis and watch the comings and goings of the yachts and know that they were really and truly on holiday. The apartment had two bedrooms suitable for the nurses and a large and beautiful living-room, with French windows on two sides leading out onto a patio and balcony, which I turned into a treatment room for them. The equipping of the new centre, which I did myself – down to the last teaspoon – and the recruiting of suitable nurses took time and thought, and much money, but by the beginning of the 1983 summer season we were ready to welcome our first six patients.

I had made contact with a charming renal consultant who was in charge of a large state renal unit in Montpellier, only seven miles away from my new holiday centre, who agreed to be honorary physician. Charles Mion was well-liked and highly-respected by his colleagues in England, so I knew I had made a wise choice. He was driving me out to lunch one day to meet some of the French kidney patients and I was sitting beside him prattling away, telling him how I felt a holiday dialysis centre should look.

'It should have an attractive, welcoming entrance, clean but not clinical, and there should be lots of light in the treatment room with flowers everywhere. Flowers on the pillowcases and on the curtains, and real flowers in vases. The nurses will wear our white T-shirts and white shorts, with long, brown legs and there will be a feeling of love and caring and understanding.'

I was carrying on in this vein when he interrupted me and, turning briefly, said, 'Do you know, it is the first time I have ever thought how nice it would be to be a dialysis patient!'

I was very concerned that the general public, not understanding the real need for holidays for dialysis patients, might perhaps think that my expenditure in this respect was frivolous. Much of the money that had been sent in support of my charity over the years had come from people who could ill afford a holiday themselves. I felt, as always, a heavy responsibility towards the generous donors to the fund and consequently was anxious to do the right thing by them. As the completion date for the centre drew nearer I constantly heard a voice in my head saying, 'If I had known you were going to spend my money on that I would never have given it to you in the first place. The South of France, whatever next?'

My relief was enormous when a letter arrived from a Guildford solicitor letting me know of the death of one of his clients, who had bequeathed her entire estate to the BKPA. He estimated the value of the estate, which included a small but attractive property in a fashionable part of Cobham, to be in excess of £100,000. 'Perhaps you would like to come over and see the property and decide what you would like done with the contents and make arrangements to put the house on the market,' he said.

Later that week Laurence and I turned into the long drive

lined with rhododendrons and azaleas with mixed feelings. Had she a husband and children and, if so, what would our reception be? If my own mother, on whom I had lavished much care and attention since the death of my father, suddenly died leaving all her worldly goods to an unknown charity I would find it difficult to feel charitable towards them myself! But within minutes of our arrival the solicitor had sat us down in a comfortably furnished sitting-room and was explaining that his client was a widow and childless; her husband had died from cancer and she had originally left her entire estate to cancer research. Eighteen months after his death she herself became a kidney patient and changed her will in favour of the BKPA. The solicitor and our benefactor's uncle were the joint trustees. Even whilst he was talking I realized that here was an end to all my worries.

Turning to the uncle I asked, 'Do you think that your niece would have liked to feel that out of the tragedy of her own death had come real happiness for other kidney patients?' I went on to tell him about my plan to purchase a property in the South of France and my fears that some of the people who had made donations might not have wished their money to be used in that way. The more I talked the more I could see that he was warming to my idea, and by the time I had finished he was ready to offer his blessing and approval. I was much relieved.

My rating amongst the renal consultants in the country was gradually improving and, with a few exceptions, most of the consultants were on friendly terms – convinced at last that my aims were genuine, even if my method of achieving them did not always meet with their approval. More and more consultants were encouraging their patients to use our holiday facilities and most of them were grateful to have the BKPA to turn to when the DHSS offered a blind eye to their obvious needs. From the opening by the Princess of Wales of the new paediatric renal unit in Glasgow through to the opening of a holiday dialysis centre in the South of France, the BKPA continued to make good headlines. Whilst, percentage-wise, my overheads continued to be well below the national average for the running of charities in this country, my staff had increased considerably. In addition to Laurence and six clerical staff I had taken on the much-needed services of a Finance Officer, and eight nursing staff for the holiday centres made up the complement.

With the completion of our first successful season at La Grande Motte I once again gave in to the pleas of the patients and flew to Malaga, with the intention of finding a suitable property for a third holiday dialysis centre in the popular town of Torremolinos. Anxious to avoid all unnecessary cost I had chosen Spain not only because of its cheapness, nor because of the large number of tour operators offering low-priced holidays in the area, but also because Clifford Turner, my incredibly generous lawyers, also had an office in Madrid. The Paris office had already undertaken the conveyancing of the property at La Grande Motte entirely free of charge and I was naturally hopeful that their office in Madrid would follow suit, and in that I was not disappointed. I spent three hectic, concentrated days viewing properties in Torremolinos and nearby Fuengirola and finally, on the third day, I chanced upon a beautiful apartment overlooking the sea, brand-new, with an impressive entrance, and not far from the shops. The price fell within my budget and in a frenzy of excitement I rang my new Spanish lawyer, Luis Rascilla, in Madrid and begged him to fly down to Malaga on the next plane and vet it for me. He dropped everything, as if I were all that mattered in his busy life, and by four o'clock that afternoon we were in the luxurious office of the developer, after a quick visit to the empty apartment. I sat there listening to their excited conversation not being able to understand a word but hugging myself with delight, knowing that once again I had found the perfect place for another holiday centre in the sun. After what seemed an interminable length of time, during which documents had been passed back and forth and the speed of the conversation had reached fever pitch, Luis turned to me and said, 'Sorry, Leez, I cannot allow you to do beezness with theeze bandeets.'

Nothing would make him alter his decision and although I was bitterly disappointed I knew I must abide by his advice. I returned home rather crestfallen and, turning my back on the Spanish mainland, decided to look in the direction of the beautiful island of Majorca. By the end of 1983 I had purchased a lovely apartment in Cala Mayor, right on the edge of the bay with a perfect view of the beach and the King's summer palace. Once again the apartment was newly built with a large treatment room letting onto a veranda above the sea. I equipped it with four dialysis stations so that we could welcome eight patients a week and, with well-furnished bedrooms for the nursing staff, I planned to open for business the following April.

At the beginning of 1983 Timbo's health was the best it had been for many years. Bonham's had once more taken him under their wing and he was running the South Atlantic Appeal Fund, for victims of the Falkland's War, with which they were deeply involved. He was living in Rose Street, near Covent Garden, in a funny little house he had got from a friend for a peppercorn rent. The apparent reason for the low rent was a draw-back in the shape of a lovely girl, five years his senior, who turned up once or twice a week and took over the spare bedroom, which she used as a *pied-à-terre* on her weekly visits to London. Timbo, a confirmed bachelor even to the point of declaring the fact to a national magazine, eventually succumbed to her undoubted charms and on 4 June that year he married her. Susy brought two lovely daughters to the wedding, giving him an added purpose to his life and two more people to boss and love! They are now his own daughters, bearing his name, and for me have become two additional and much-loved grandchildren. Susy, a Titian-haired beauty with brains and single-mindedness, transformed Timbo in a matter of months into a family man; a transformation I feared I would never see.

Nigel and I had flown out to Singapore the previous year to

spend a little time with Becky. Despite a brave face and lots of fun shared, we realized that she was not happy and that her marriage was a complete disaster. Consequently I was sad, but not surprised, to hear her voice on the telephone a few months later sounding suspiciously close.

'Hello Mum, guess where I am?'

'Heathrow?' I asked.

'No,' she replied. 'I'm back in the flat in Richmond.'

The following year her divorce came through and I thought of all the unnecessary pain and hurt that had been caused by her marriage to Gary, but we had weathered the storm and still loved each other and perhaps were wiser, if not richer, from the experience. Timbo's engagement came as a fearful shock to her and, coming as it did at such a difficult time in her own life, caused her great unhappiness. Her place as his confidant companion had been taken by another and she felt rejected and broken-hearted. For so many years she had been deeply involved in his life, sharing flats, visiting him in hospital, supporting him when he was ill and lonely and living alone, sharing their friends, their jokes and laugher and suddenly it seemed she was no longer needed at a time when, for once, she actually needed him. It was a difficult, sensitive time for all of us and I felt for her very deeply.

# 10

# 'Say Not, the Struggle Nought Availeth'

I suppose I was naïve in the extreme to imagine that public awareness of a situation where kidney patients were being sentenced to death by an inadequate Health Service would automatically ensure a reprieve for some of the many hundreds of Britain's kidney patients destined to die each year. The responsibility for the lives of these patients had been bandied about between the DHSS at the Elephant and Castle and the various Regional Health Authorities and I thought the time had come to try to establish once and for all where the responsibility lay. The DHSS had always claimed, with a certain amount of unjustifiable pride, that they never dictated to the Regions how they were to dispense their allotted funds. The Chairmen and officers of the RHAs persisted in their reasonable claim that since the DHSS would not give them sufficient funds to maintain their programme of high-cost speciality medicine properly it was useless to impress upon them the need to ensure that all renal patients requiring dialysis and transplantation should receive it.

Knowing our Prime Minister to be a strong and forthright person, and thinking her to be caring and compassionate towards her fellow men, I had taken the bull by the horns and written to her, describing in detail the horrifying situation and begging for her intervention. I finished the letter boldly: 'The British Kidney Patient Association gives all the financial assistance within its power to relieve the present situation but cannot put an end to this tragic, wicked waste of life, only you it seems can do that now. I appeal to you on behalf of kidney patients throughout the country either to instruct the Chancellor to make more money available to the Regional Health Authorities for specific allocation to the Renal Replacement Programme or insist that the programme is funded centrally.'

The reply from the Prime Minister's private secretary, William Rickett, was disappointing, and after a long explanation as to why it would not be feasible for the Programme to be funded centrally he closed with the words: 'The Prime Minister appreciates the special position of end-stage renal failure services as providing a proven method of treatment for an otherwise fatal condition. However, Health Authorities are also aware of this and it is their responsibility to take it into account in deciding between competing claims for available funds, including the claims of the other services you mention.' Since there were no extra funds of any significance being made available it was of purely academic interest to know that, in the opinion of the Prime Minister, the responsibility for the treatment of patients in end-stage renal failure lay with the Regional Health Authorities.

Over the years I had been personally responsible for saving the lives of a number of patients whose relatives had alerted me, usually by telephone, to the fact that their loved one was not going to receive treatment. I had in all but one case been able to arrange for their treatment in other NHS units mostly, I'm ashamed to say, the same unit, whose consultants had shown compassionate understanding towards the older patient and the patient with other medical problems. In all but three cases the help had come too late, since the deterioration in the patients' health was so advanced that dialysis was unable to give them more than a few extra months of life. My concern was for those patients whose relatives did not understand that the words, 'I'm afraid, Mrs Hunt, in your husband's case, dialysis would not be the answer', meant in truth, 'I'm afraid, Mrs Hunt, that because of the shortage of facilities we are not able to offer treatment to all patients who require it and we have decided that your husband cannot be one of the lucky ones'. As a result many, many patients were slipping through my net.

Because of my fearless approach and my proclaimed dictum that 'the patient comes first', when I was alerted it was often sufficient for me to write a friendly letter to the patient's consultant along the lines of: 'I have received an anxious telephone call from the wife of your patient John Hunt, expressing her fears that her husband will not receive dialysis treatment when he needs it because of his age, so I hope so much that when they next attend clinic you will give her your reassurance and convince her that her fears are groundless.'

Many patients, of course, were not at the mercy of the renal consultant but had been turned down by their GP or hospital consultant on the grounds that their age, physical disability, or whatever the reason the doctors felt appropriate, would not warrant such expensive and complicated treatment as dialysis. Needless to say, neither the patients themselves nor their relatives were ever faced with the truth, thus not only robbing them of the opportunity to seek help elsewhere but also of the chance to raise their voice in protest.

I had let it be known through the media that the BKPA intended to cover the cost of private dialysis treatment for a patient who had been turned down by the Health Service, but the problem was to find such a patient. The press were constantly ringing me and asking me to give them the name of a patient being denied treatment and I was forever explaining that no patient *knew* that he was being denied treatment, and that until the need for treatment arose treatment was not required, and once the need arose and treatment was denied, then the patient died within a reasonably short space of time. I was obsessed with the thought of the wicked waste of life, the distress of the patients, and the agony of those that loved them. It is one thing to visit your son in hospital knowing that all is being done to save his life, and quite another to visit him fearing that it is not.

On my return from a week's holiday, on January 4 1985, I
arrived back in my office at 3.30 p.m. that Friday afternoon.
Because of my absence there were a great number of letters
for me to deal with, messages to read, and phone calls to
make, so I set aside a written message from my secretary
stating that a certain Michael Hall, the warden of a hostel for
the homeless in Oxford, had rung constantly over the past
two days wishing to speak to me urgently. Since I had a
telephone number for him where I could ring after office
hours I finally got through to him at six o'clock that Friday
evening. He was clearly in a desperate state. One of the
residents in his hostel, a man of forty-four called Derek Sage,
who had been dialysing at a local renal unit for eighteen
months, had suddenly been denied all further treatment. The
consultant in charge of his case had rung Mike Hall two days
before and had told him that the dialysis that Derek had just
received in their unit on New Year's Eve was to be his last. He
went on to say that the patient was dirty, noisy, disruptive
and that his nurses had refused to treat him any more, and as
he was afraid of losing his nurses he had no alternative but to
discontinue treatment.

Mike Hall's horror was genuine when he went on to tell me
that his protest had brought forth an adamant refusal on the
part of the doctor to reconsider his decision and the
suggestion that he should make his complaint through the
normal hospital channels. He immediately rang the hospital
administrator and reported the conversation that he had had
with the consultant, at the same time expressing his disgust
and disbelief that a man who had been receiving treatment for
more than a year should be condemned to death by an NHS
consultant simply because he found him unacceptable as a
patient. The administrator promised to look into the matter
immediately, and rang back to say that the reason why the
patient was being refused further treatment was not what
Mike Hall had been told – a reason which, in fact, the
consultant later denied ever having given – but because the
quality of his life was unacceptable. Mike's protests were, if

possible, even louder. How could the doctor who had never seen him outside the renal unit possibly be in a position to decide on the quality of his life? Derek was a much-loved member of their small community, who thoroughly enjoyed life despite his dreaded visits to the renal unit and had himself announced his wish to continue living. Dr Hilary Allinson, the local GP, attended the hostel regularly and saw Derek almost daily but had never been consulted by the renal consultant as to the quality of Derek's life. It was obvious to both the consultant and the hospital administrator that there was trouble ahead for them if the tune were not changed quickly, so at the third attempt the consultant came up with another reason – and this was Derek's deteriorating physical and mental condition.

I listened to this horrifying story but could not really bring myself to believe that any renal consultant would dare to play such games, and I felt there must be more to the story than met the eye. I told Mike I would do what I could to help him but as it was already Friday evening it might be difficult for me to arrange anything before Monday. At this point Mike almost broke down. He told me that the renal doctor had said it was unlikely that Derek would live beyond Monday as they had been under-dialysing him for some time with a view, presumably, to killing him. It was imperative, he said, that I made arrangements for a Monday dialysis and even then he wasn't sure whether Derek would make it. I told him I would ring back after talking to Hilary Allinson, Derek's GP. I had expected to hear from the GP that Derek had some fearful, irreversible medical condition or multi-system disease that Mike was not aware of, so I was very surprised to have her confirm all that he had said to me. She added that she had rung the doctor herself in a final attempt to persuade him to take Derek back on the programme, and she also confirmed Mike's estimation of his quality of life, his desire to live, and finished with the declaration that contrary to the renal physician's assessment of his medical condition there had been no change in his health over the past four months.

By this time I had been much affected by the distress of these two obviously genuine people and shared their disgust, disbelief, and horror at the turn of events. I had heard, of course, of patients being selected out of treatment and I knew of patients who had not been returned to dialysis after a failed transplant. I had even met and spoken with, before she died, a patient on peritoneal dialysis in a local hospital whose nearest renal unit had turned their back on her, unable to take her on to the programme through lack of facilities. But I had never ever come across a case where a patient whose life was being sustained by haemodialysis, who was able to get off his bed and leave the hospital on his own two feet to lead an independent life, was having his life-saving treatment terminated.

I knew what I had to do, but I was fearful for Timbo's sake and my own. The unit where this drama was taking place was the same unit where Timbo had received Nigel's kidney and one of the consultants in question part of the team looking after him. I rang Timbo and warned him but he said, as really I knew he would, 'Of course you must go ahead and try and save this man's life. Don't worry about me.' I knew there would be repercussions and that in no time they would forget that I was the mother of a kidney patient in their care, with the same needs and fears as the mothers of their other patients, but I could not possibly stand by and let this man die without lifting a finger to help him and, besides, there was a matter of principle at stake.

It was nine o'clock by the time I got through to Dr John Moorhead at his home. John had been a friend for some years and as well as being the consultant in charge of the renal unit at the Royal Free Hospital in London he also had a private renal practice at the Hospital of St John and St Elizabeth in Maida Vale. I told John the whole story and admired him enormously for his own courage, since to give refuge to a patient of a colleague who had closed his door on him was surely breaking with the tradition of the medical profession which says: 'No matter what justifiable criticism is levelled at us we must stand shoulder to shoulder and keep a united front.'

I arranged with John that Derek would be dialysed at the Hospital of St John and St Elizabeth on Monday morning and I asked him to do all in his power to save Derek's life, since I realized from my conversation with Hilary Allinson that by Monday his life would be hanging in the balance. Before I went to bed that night, troubled but determined, I rang my friend James Wilkinson of BBC television; next day, the story broke.

I had no personal feeling of animosity towards the consultant in charge, or the nursing staff, who had mistakenly thought that this homeless man could be quietly and conveniently disposed of, but I was absolutely determined that nothing like it would ever occur again in a British renal unit. A disgusting article was printed in *The Lancet* by a young barrister called Diana Brahams who had somehow got access to the patient's medical notes. Derek was described in this article in the same way as a Nazi might have painted a picture of a German Jew. His behaviour, apparently, was less than human, incontinent, foul-mouthed, and abusive, and yet in all the four and a half months that he was treated three times a week at the Hospital of St John and St Elizabeth not once did he display any of the behaviour patterns that had nearly cost him his life. Inarticulate and simple, driven by fear like a crazed animal, he had voiced his protest in the only way known to him. No one with a streak of human feeling could have failed to have been more than moved, deeply disturbed, by the thought of the utter wretchedness of that poor, misunderstood human being.

Derek's health continued to improve under the loving care of the nursing staff in London and arrangements were being made for him to have home dialysis in the hostel when the news was broken to him of his mother's death. The news was more than his poor old heart could take. The following morning the departure of his brother, the bearer of such sad tidings, he was found unconscious in his bed and taken to the

Hospital of St John and St Elizabeth, where he died two days later without regaining consciousness, surrounded by people who cared. The bill to the Association for his treatment over the four months came to nearly £10,000, and not once have I ever regretted one single penny of the money spent, nor the price that I have personally had to pay as a result of answering a plea for help. Derek died, in fact, not of renal failure but from a massive coronary, knowing that he was loved and held a rightful place in our society.

For many years, as I have mentioned, and as that story illustrates, I had been deeply concerned that the truth was being withheld from the patient and his relatives concerning the seriousness of his condition and the true reasons for lack of treatment, so that when I was invited to be one of the speakers at a symposium held in November 1985 on the subject of renal failure, arranged by the London Medical Group, a student group who study issues raised by the practice of medicine, I accepted eagerly. Here was my chance to air the problem that had been perturbing me for some time.

I told the students that a general physician of long standing recently shared his problem with me and asked for my opinion. One of his regular visits was to a terminal cancer patient who persistently asked him when she could expect to get better. He had confided the seriousness of his patient's illness to her husband, who had begged him to keep the true facts to himself. He felt uncomfortable in the presence of his patient and dreaded his weekly visits. What would I do, he asked? My immediate reaction was that he should, of course, tell his patient the truth, and I wondered why he had withheld it in the first place. In entering into a conspiracy with the husband, he had put himself quite unnecessarily into a most unenviable position, had broken trust with the very person whose trust he enjoyed, and, furthermore, had presumed that her husband was right in thinking that his wife would wish the knowledge of her impending death to be withheld from her. It might well have been that the wife would have chosen to withhold the truth from her husband, but she was denied that choice. Surely, I said, the basis of a good relationship between doctor and patient relies on trust, and trust is based on truth. The joy of truth is that it is so simple, so black and white. No longer need the doctor concern himself with whether or not his patient is emotionally or physically strong enough to stand the truth. The patient need no longer anxiously study the doctor's face, trying to decide if the truth is being spoken.

The truth can be told with imagination and compassion, prefaced with the words 'in my opinion', thus leaving a ray of hope for those who cannot face it. I have a file in my office, shamefully thick, with letters from patients and those that love them filled with a mixture of anguish and abuse, worry and heartache, which would never have been written if the writers had been sure that the truth had been told them.

I told the students that I was at the moment heavily involved with a number of tragic cases concerning the deaths of renal patients in unfortunate circumstances, whose relatives were seeking retribution. My task, as I saw it, was to allay the fears, soften the criticism, and help these unfortunate people to come to terms with their loss in the belief that death was inevitable. I knew the truth, no matter how unpalatable, would have been found acceptable and their wounds would have healed over leaving no scars, but whilst the dead rested in peace those left behind were restlessly seeking the truth. Some 2,000 kidney patients annually die of end-stage renal failure in this country, and they die not because treatment is unknown, but because the Health Service is underfunded and insufficient money is being put to the Renal Replacement Programme and, therefore, no treatment is being made available for them. How could this possibly be the fault of the renal physicians and, if it is not, why should they take it upon themselves to carry the blame? Why should they feel it necessary to cover up for an inadequate Health Service and pull the wool over the eyes of the relatives and patients, telling them that dialysis treatment would not solve the problem, or save the patient's life, when they know that the truth is that it would? The patient has the right to know that in an ideal world he would, of course, receive dialysis treatment even if no promises could be made as to how long the treatment would prolong his life.

I told them I felt that renal physicians took too much upon themselves and so had become accustomed to making decisions concerning the future of their patients – and whether indeed they will have a future at all – without consultation even with the close relatives of the patient, let alone the patient himself. Surely, I argued, only the patient himself was in a position to decide whether or not he wished treatment to be given in the first place, to be continued, or to be terminated.

I had looked quite closely into three other areas of medicine where life/death decisions would be made by physicians but, on the whole, were not. Patients with cerebral palsy, spinal injuries, and terminal cancer were administered to by doctors who told me they would seldom consider not treating initially, and that they only withdrew treatment after consultation with the relatives and, where possible, with the patient themselves. The 'quality of life' was never given as a reason for not treating, despite the fact that to the onlooker the quality of life of all these patients was far less enviable than that of the patient on renal dialysis. What then could have been the reasons for the attitudes and behaviour of the physicians looking after renal patients differing so greatly from those caring for patients in other fields of medicine?

I explained that I thought the shortage of facilities for the treatment of patients with end-stage renal failure was forcing the renal physicians to practise selection. They lived in an isolated medical world, cut off from their colleagues, destined to treat the same patients year after year until their deaths. They were, quite rightly, proud of the kingdom that they ruled, anxious to produce fitter patients, better figures, more transplants than their competitors, and took as a personal failure their inability to treat all patients who were referred to them in need of treatment. Perhaps that was why they felt it

necessary to hide the truth and give reasons for the denial of
treatment based on their own judgement – and not on lack of
facilities, which was outside their control.

I ended by suggesting that no blame could be attached to
the doctor unable to offer life-saving treatment to his patient
because of lack of facilities, but could he not be blamed for
concealing the truth, not only from the patient and those that
loved him, but also from those agencies both eager and able
to help? If we were ever to see the day when the only criterion
for treatment was the need for it and the patients and their
relatives were given the weapons with which to fight for it,
then we must have the truth, the whole truth, and nothing but
the truth.

Much water has flowed under my bridge since that day, more
than nineteen years ago, when Timbo was first diagnosed as a
kidney patient. Some of the water had been dark and
troubled, threatening to drag me down into its depths, but
much has been light and sparkling, reflecting happiness and
laughter and the faces of people who care. I have so much to
be grateful for and so many people to thank: surrounded by
love and kindness, cushioned against the harder knocks by
my own buoyant personality. I have been helped and
encouraged to replace the sadness in my own life with
happiness in the lives of other people. I have made many
friends amongst the medical profession and, surprisingly
perhaps, few enemies. I have been spoiled by Health
Ministers and Secretaries of State, who have generously
given me their time and attention and treated my campaigning with respect.

I have worked very hard over the past ten years to build up
a charity based on sound foundations which will still be in
existence long after I have gone. It is my dearest wish that
fifty years from now the BKPA will be standing shoulder to
shoulder with The Spastics Society, The British Diabetic
Association, and similar medical charities founded to give
practical support to unfortunate people suffering from

specific disabilities and disease. I want so much for there always to be not only somewhere, but someone, to turn to when things get rough and life becomes seemingly impossible for those trying to walk tall and pull their weight in the community. I know it will be difficult but I hope that those running the BKPA in the future will not forget the value of personal contact and remember that many, many patients, whilst thanking me for the cheque they have received, have expressed their relief in knowing that there is someone behind them who has shared many of their difficulties and can see the problems from their own point of view.

I have been terribly fortunate in the support that I have been given, and as a result I have been able to alter significantly the lives of many of the patients for the better and to give considerable financial aid to renal units throughout the country. It would have made little difference how much I had cared, or understood, or desperately wanted to help, if I had not had the generous backing of so many people who also cared and understood. If I have been successful in accomplishing some of the things I have set my heart on over the past ten years, then I owe that success to Timbo, for making me aware of the problems, and to many hundreds of others for helping me to solve them.

As for the family, amazingly enough they have all survived, not only as individuals but as a strong, loving family unit. Whilst they are none of them rash enough to enquire too deeply into my day to day trials, tribulations, and triumphs they are nevertheless at times politely interested, and I ask no more of them. They have been long suffering in the extreme, in the face of my deep involvement with the problems concerning only one member of the family, and whilst I have tried very hard to be fair in my dealings with all of them it has not always been that simple. When your only son cannot make up his mind whether to die on this Monday or the next it is difficult to feign interest in the achievements of your youngest daughter in her drama class. By the same token it is almost impossible to absorb the true significance of the christening of your first grandchild when her uncle and godfather has refused the offer of a wheelchair and is physically struggling to get to the font on his own two feet. When your elder daughter accuses you of not caring what becomes of her, it is not always easy to see beyond the fact that she is not only beautiful but has her health, which her only brother lost when just a boy. I make no excuses for myself, but it was always hard to remember that Nigel, in his own way, needed me as much as Timbo did. Because I identified myself with Nigel I assumed that, because Timbo was our son, his feelings would be the same as mine, but he is, after all, Timbo's father and a man, and I am his mother and a woman, and I should have understood the difference.

Despite their early difficulties my daughters are living full and satisfying lives. Susie is a partner in a firm of solicitors at Winchester and has made her home only ten miles away from mine, and with Katherine and Charles at boarding-school life has become much easier for her. Becky, who is an account executive with a large public relations company in London, lives a gay and exciting life surrounded by gay and exciting friends, with a good job to help keep her feet somewhere near the ground. Timbo is busy fighting the rejection of Nigel's kidney with his usual optimism and good humour and, whilst it is some weeks since he has been able to get to his office at Cazenove, where he now works, he is determined that his present problems will be solved in the not too distant future. As for Nigel, he is leading a full and normal life, proving that it is perfectly possible to live satisfactorily on one kidney.

Mercifully Timbo's sense of humour has not deserted him and Becky reported a recent conversation which illustrates this.

The plan is now that Timbo should receive another cadaver kidney whilst there is still some function remaining in the kidney he received from his father. Becky pointed out that there was a much greater chance of success if he were to have one of *her* kidneys.

'It would be quite wrong to use Mummy's, even if Peter

(Morris) were prepared to take it,' she said, 'as she will be much more use to you standing upright on her feet; but mine would be much better than a cadaver kidney and I want you to have it.'

Timbo refused as she had not yet had any children, and so said he would not dream of accepting a kidney from her, but Becky was insistent. 'Surely you wouldn't be so crazy in a life or death situation to refuse?'

'Oh well,' he replied, 'if we are talking about a life or death situation, that is quite another matter. Of course you know I would take both of them and visit your grave daily with flowers!'

As I look back over the years and watch the struggles of my only son to lead a full and useful life I am filled not only with pride and admiration, but also with a feeling of gratitude that I have been privileged to share in some of his struggles and watch his development from a young football-kicking boy into a man of worth. He is truly representative of hundreds of kidney patients throughout the country whose courage must be an inspiration to us all, but I am his mother so perhaps I will be forgiven if I raise my glass in tribute – to Timbo, man of the match.

# 11

# The Final Chapter

The end when it came was swift and painless. Our only sadness was that after all the long years of waiting to say goodbye, Nigel and I were on holiday in Mallorca that Friday evening at 9.15 on September 11th 1987.

Timbo had come down with his family and spent the day with us at Oakhanger shortly before we left on our three week summer break. After the failure of Nigel's kidney he was back once more on peritoneal dialysis, which seemed to suit him, and apart from the fact that he was very tired, he was his usual bright and sunny self, full of optimism and crazy plans for the near future and seeing ahead to two years when he would sell his London house and move out into the country, which he loved. It seems so strange now, looking back on that day, to know that he only had two weeks left with us on this earth.

The week before he died I rang him from Mallorca to make sure all was well and he glossed over the difficulties he was having with his dialysis, showing much more interest and concern in the problems facing his dialysis sister at St Philip's; she was desperately short of staff because of lack of funds to pay them and feared for the welfare of her patients. We discussed together possible ways in which the BKPA might be able to help and with his usual 'Love to Dad,' we said goodbye to one another for the last time.

As our little boat nosed her way towards the shore late that Friday afternoon, it seemed nothing could disturb the even tenor of our sun drenched days; and then I heard the telephone. Through the window that opens out onto the shore below, the dull persistent tone rang out – I can hear it still. I had no sense of urgency, no sense of panic, and not once did Timbo cross my mind. On reaching the house, I rang the office and asked them what the trouble was. I was told that all was well, but Becky had been trying to contact me all afternoon, and would I ring her at her office. Still no anxiety or apprehension, just the realisation that it was Friday and we usually had a chat together before the coming weekend. When I finally got through, I was ill-prepared for the tone of her voice. 'Boots?', her favourite name for me, 'I'm afraid our boy is not very well.' Timbo had apparently been admitted to hospital at three o'clock the previous morning with another episode of peritonitis. By that Thursday evening it was obvious that he was not responding to treatment and was causing alarm and concern to those looking after him, which included his friend and surgeon, Christopher Rudge. By Friday morning his condition had worsened and Becky was alerted by his wife. She went to the hospital and saw and spoke with both Chris and Timbo's doctor, Martin Mansell, who advised her to contact us and bring us home. Poor little Becky, she was so frightened and so alone and began frantically trying to contact us who, blissfully unaware of the drama taking place at home, were bobbing happily carefree on the warm and brilliant waters of the Mediterranean.

Our conversation together was tight and urgent; we were both controlled and terrified. The plan, she told me, was to operate on Timbo that evening at six o'clock in the desperate hope that maybe a perforated gut, which could be mended, was the cause for the overwhelming peritonitis which had now been complicated by double pneumonia. After five unsuccessful attempts to contact Chris on the telephone, I finally spoke with him shortly before the operation was to take place. Chris explained the situation to me in clear strong terms, hiding nothing, and certainly not his own opinion that the operation was Timbo's only chance of survival. 'Do you

think, Chris, you might lose him on the table?' I asked.
'Heavens, I hope not,' came the reply. He promised he would
ring me in two to three hours' time and Nigel and I settled
down to wait. Although Timbo by that time was unconscious, Becky, I know, had kissed him for us both before he
went off to theatre, so that he would know how near we were
to him, although so far away.

We sat on the patio talking of other things while the sun
sank behind the island of Dragonera, and the night closed in;
the waiting seemed interminable. I prayed only that God
would take care of him and do what was best for him and I
felt calm and comforted. It was 9.15 at home when I could
bear the waiting no longer and I rose to telephone. Nigel's
voice broke in on my thoughts. 'We mustn't worry, it must be
good news that Chris hasn't rung us yet. I expect he has found
something wrong which he is able to put right. He would have
rung us sooner if nothing could be done.' I lifted the
telephone and dialled the number and was put through
without delay to the ICU. 'It's Timbo's mother here,' I said.
'May I have a word with my daughter, please, I think she is
waiting for him to return from theatre.' The reply which came
hit me like a bullet from a gun. 'Oh! Mrs Ward, I have some
terrible news for you, I'm afraid Timbo has just died . . . hold
on a moment, please.' The voice was female and charged with
emotion and with the words spoken pounding through my
head, I hung on to that cold impersonal plastic mouthpiece
through which the news had come, calling out for what
seemed forever, 'Oh no, no, please don't go away, tell me
what has happened. He can't be dead. Tell me please, don't go
away. Oh someone come, somebody speak to me, please,'
until finally Chris's voice on the end of the phone confirmed
the awful words that I had heard. Immediately following his
forty-second operation, the heart of my beloved Timbo had
ceased to beat.

Then followed the confusion, the disbelief and vain
attempts to comfort his shattered sister and his wife across
hundreds and hundreds of miles of emptiness. Nigel and I,

with their approval, decided to stay on for a few days and make all the necessary harrowing arrangements from a safe distance. I rang Trevor Huddleston, who was in the Moorfields Eye Hospital recovering from an operation. 'Please, Trevor – tell me, where do you think Timbo is now?' Trevor's words, so strong and sure, will stay with me forever. 'I don't just think,' he said, 'I know, he is in Paradise, where free and unrestricted he can grow to his full height.'

I was in constant touch with Becky, whose grief was agonising for us both to bear, and her pain at facing the prospect of a life which had never known his absence, helped me to face my own. Nigel, who loved him so, fused with me over those four long days, so that we became one person with a single wound, striving to find a healing salve. We cried and laughed and reminisced under a cloudless sky, and the air was full of 'Do you remember the time when . . . ?', 'I wonder what he really meant . . . ?', 'Why do you think he said . . . ?' and, of course, the words 'if only' prefaced many of our longings shared.

By the time we returned to England we knew that Timbo had been sent here for a purpose and had left us only because the job was done. Had he survived, the future was bleak in all respects, and we knew really that all our prayers had been answered; he had died peacefully, without pain or fear, at a time when his natural optimism was at its height, loved, respected and admired, and we could not ask for more.

The Thanksgiving Service for his life, which was held at St James's Church, Piccadilly, on the 7th October that year, gave proof to the affection and high regard in which he was held by many. Nigel and I were deeply touched and filled with pride that men and women of worth and purpose from near and far should have left their hospitals, schools, offices and homes to pay tribute to the short life of our only son.

Some five years ago, before a visit to Australia, we were discussing my intention to have a service of thanksgiving for his life had he died while he was away from home. 'You must do what you like,' he had said, 'but don't do it for my sake!

The idea of a whole lot of people coming together saying how wonderful I was, when they could hardly say anything else, seems rather stupid, and anyway, how would you feel if nobody turned up?'

Certainly when the time came, as I stood surrounded by his many friends and admirers, there was no room for sadness in my heart, only joy at having had, known and loved him, and as I lifted my voice with theirs in thanksgiving, Timbo was there with me throughout the service, as he will be, I know, until the end of my days.

# Index